394.268
H   Harper, Wilhelmina
              The harvest feast

Date Due

Collection of twenty-six selections includes stories and poems about Pilgrims and the first Thanksgiving as well as stories and poems about celebrating Thanksgiving today.

The Harvest Feast

New, Revised Edition

The
Harvest Feast

Stories of Thanksgiving
Yesterday and Today

Compiled by Wilhelmina Harper

Illustrated by W. T. Mars

E. P. DUTTON & CO., INC., NEW YORK

to Marguerite Vance

Compiler's Note

The Harvest Feast was originally compiled to fill a real need for a collection of stories and poems about America's own holiday, Thanksgiving. I have revised *The Harvest Feast,* and have added several new selections.

My chief purpose in compiling this book has been to present to boys and girls of today the cherished traditions of Thanksgiving in the hope that this day of feasting and prayer will be more meaningful to them. There are tales that picture those stirring Thanksgivings of yesterday; of the boys and girls who came over on the *Mayflower;* of the first Thanksgiving when the Pilgrims and the Indians met in peaceful celebration. And there are stories of more modern times, stories of adventure and of fact and fancy. Among the new selections will be found Carolyn Sherwin Bailey's delightful "A Basket for

Thanksgiving," describing a long ago harvest time in New Hampshire; the warm and humorous "The Thanksgiving Goose" by Elizabeth Hough Sechrist; and "A New Pioneer" by Dorothy Canfield Fisher, telling of a brave Austrian child and her adjustment to American life. Also there are new poems by Rowena Bennett, Elizabeth Coatsworth, and Nancy Byrd Turner.

This volume will be one of year-around usefulness in libraries, schools, and homes, and the story-teller will recognize its value as she searches for suitable stories to tell during the autumn season.

W. H.

Acknowledgments

The compiler makes grateful acknowledgment to the following publishers and authors for the courtesies granted in the use of copyrighted selections and others:

Appleton-Century and to The St. Nicholas Magazine for "The Black Sheep's Coat" by Cornelia Meigs; "A Thanksgiving Dinner That Flew Away" by Hezekiah Butterworth from *Our Holidays Retold From St. Nicholas;* and for "The Kingdom of the Greedy" by P. J. Stahl from *Story Hour Favorites* by Wilhelmina Harper.

The American Boy Magazine for "Old Tom's Thanksgiving Dinner" by William T. Whitlock.

Rowena Bennett for "If I Were a Pilgrim Child."

The Bobbs-Merrill Company for "When the Frost is on the Punkin" from *Neighborly Poems* by James Whitcomb Riley, copyright 1891, 1929.

Milton Bradley Company for "The Last Thursday in November" from *Stories of the World's Holidays* by Grace Humphrey.

Child Life Magazine for "Indian Summer" by Cornelia Meigs; and for "Indians for Thanksgiving" by Dorothy Heiderstadt.

Thomas Y. Crowell Company for "Boys and Girls of the *Mayflower*" from *The First Year* by Enid LaMonte Meadowcroft.

E. P. Dutton & Company, Inc., for "A Quick-Running Squash" from *Short Stories for Short People* by Alicia Aspinwall.

Harcourt, Brace & World, Inc., for "The Huckabuck Family" from *Rootabaga Pigeons* by Carl Sandburg, copyright 1923 by Harcourt, Brace & World, Inc.

The Estate of Oliver Herford for "A Thanksgiving Fable."

Lothrop, Lee & Shepard Company for "The Pumpkin Giant" from *The Pot of Gold* by Mary Wilkins Freeman.

The Macmillan Company for "Becky's Thanksgiving Turkey" from *Becky Landers* by Constance Lindsay Skinner; and for "November" from *Twelve Months Make a Year* by Elizabeth Coatsworth, copyright 1943 by The Macmillan Company.

Macrae Smith Company for "The Thanksgiving Goose" from *It's Time for Thanksgiving* by Elizabeth Hough Sechrist and Janette Woolsey.

Rand McNally & Company for "The First New England Dinner" from *Little Pioneers* by Maude Radford Warren.

Sarah F. Scott for "A New Pioneer" (originally titled "Thanksgiving Day") from *Nothing Ever Happens* by Dorothy Canfield Fisher.

Charles Scribner's Sons for "Ezra's Thanksgivin' Out West" from *A Little Book of Profitable Tales* by Eugene Field.

Frederick A. Stokes Company for "Massasoit and His Men" from *All Through the Year* by Annette Wynne, copyright 1932.

Story Parade Inc., for "Goody O'Grumpity" by Carol Ryrie Brink.

Nancy Byrd Turner for "Indian Children Long Ago."

The Viking Press for "A Basket for Thanksgiving" from *Children of the Handcrafts* by Carolyn Sherwin Bailey, copyright 1935 by Carolyn Sherwin Bailey, copyright 1962 by Rebecca Davies Ryan.

Special thanks for many kindly courtesies extended are due to the following authors and editors: Carol R. Brink, Dorothy Heiderstadt, Cornelia Meigs, Elizabeth Hough Sechrist, Constance L. Skinner, Marjorie Barrows, Barbara Nolen and Anne Stoddard.

The compiler wishes to express her great appreciation to Lee Anna Deadrick and Abigail Lefkowitz of E. P. Dutton & Company for their valuable assistance in the preparation of this book, and to Janet Lauer, Jean Sherwood, and Val Hamilton of the Redwood City (California) Public Library Children's Room for all their interest and assistance.

Contents

  * The selections thus marked are especially suited to the enjoyment of younger children.

11

12   *Contents*

Massasoit and His Men

Annette Wynne

Massasoit and his men
Loved that first Thanksgiving Day.
"Look, he is talking to the Great Spirit,"
They said, when the governor began to pray.

The women had baked for days and days,
And there were things to eat
That were brand-new to Indians,
And they thought it all a treat.

Oh, there were games and races
And singing loud and hearty,
And the Indians liked the Pilgrims well,
At that first Thanksgiving Party.

Boys and Girls of the *Mayflower*

Enid L. Meadowcroft

The *Mayflower* rocked and tossed on the waves. In the sky a black cloud grew larger and larger. Lightning flashed. The wind whistled and cried.

"Get below, Giles Hopkins," called a man as he ran along the deck. He stopped to speak to a boy who held fast to the railing.

"I don't mind getting wet," the boy answered. "It's so crowded in the cabin and half the people are seasick."

"Never mind that. It's not safe here. And you are in the way."

"Let me help, then, Master Howland. I'm big enough," said Giles. But John Howland had already turned to go.

Suddenly the rain came. The boat tipped until it seemed to be lying on its side. The deck slanted so that the boy could hardly stand. He clung to the railing and

14

shut his eyes to keep out the sight of the water that was so near. When he looked again the boat had righted herself. But John Howland had disappeared.

Giles ran to the side of the vessel. There was his friend in the water, splashing and yelling. A great wave rolled over his head and seemed to swallow him.

On the deck at the boy's feet lay a coil of rope. One end of it hung over the side of the ship.

"The rope! Grab the rope!" called Giles. He saw Howland grasp it and then disappear again under another wave.

Giles turned and ran down the deck. "Help!" he yelled. "Help! Help! Man overboard!"

Several of the sailors came running in answer to his cry. They grabbed the rope and pulled on it. John Howland still clung to the other end. But it was a long rope and he was far from the ship.

The men pulled him through the water as though he were a fish. Then slowly, slowly they pulled him up the side of the boat. He dangled at the end of the rope like a wet rag doll. The angry waves beat against him.

Then one of the sailors grabbed a large boat hook. He reached over the side of the ship and caught it in Howland's clothes. So with the rope and the hook they tugged and pulled until they had him safe on board.

"Oh!" gasped John Howland when he could speak. "I have been nearer land than any of you. And I swallowed most of the ocean. There can't be much left between us and America now."

Then he saw Giles standing near. The boy's hair lay

flat on his head. Water streamed down his face and clothes. He was as wet as if he, too, had been overboard.

"You saved my life, boy," said Howland. "If you hadn't got help it would have been the end of me. I couldn't have held on another minute in that sea. Now will you go below?"

"Yes, sir," said Giles. He watched for a minute while the men helped Howland to the steerage. Then he started down the ladder to the cabin.

It was almost dark in the cabin. The little ship still rolled and tossed. It was not yet safe to light the oil lamps or the candles.

All day the ship had been thrown about by the great waves. Everything in the cabin was upset. Boxes and cases would not stay in place. They slid back and forth across the cabin floor with each toss of the ship.

Some of the littlest children cried with fear. Many of them had been fastened in their bunks so that they would not be hurt by the sliding boxes, or be thrown to the floor when the ship pitched.

The older boys and girls took care of the younger ones, or they sat on benches at the long table in the center of the room and told each other stories.

Many of the women lay in their bunks too ill to move. Others who were well enough tried to care for them. They clung to the bunks and to the table as they walked about. They tried to keep out of the way of the sliding boxes and ran into each other.

Giles went to his mother, who sat on the edge of her bunk. A little girl was asleep in her lap.

"Where have you been, my son?" asked Mistress Hopkins. "I sent your sister to look for you some time ago. But Constance said she could not find you. You are very wet. What have you been doing?"

"I was on the main deck," the boy answered. "Master Howland slipped and fell overboard, but he grabbed a rope that hung over the side and we pulled him up. They have taken him to the steerage to dry him out. I was the one who called for help and got the men. He said I saved his life," Giles added proudly.

"Then I suppose it is a good thing you were there," said Mistress Hopkins. "Although I heard your father tell you to stay below today. Now change your clothes at once. There are some dry ones in our box if you can find it. I saw it slide under Mistress White's bunk a minute ago. If I move to help you little Mary will wake and she has just dropped off to sleep. Her poor mother is much too ill to care for her."

"It seems to me that almost everyone is sick," said Giles. "I'm glad the sea doesn't make me feel that way. I'm hungry."

"You'll get little to eat tonight, my boy. Just a bit of smoked beef and some bread. No one has been able to light a fire all day. With the boat pitching so, it is not safe. Hurry now and get yourself dry or you will be sick, too," said Mistress Hopkins.

"Yes, Mother," replied Giles. He pulled the box from under a bunk nearby. Then he took out some dry clothes and went to the men's quarters to change.

After several days the rain stopped. The wind died

down and the sea was calm. It was cold, but the sun shone. Sails were raised again and the *Mayflower* sped on her way across the ocean.

Everyone felt better. The children had been shut up in the cabin for many days. Just to see and feel the sun made them race about the decks and shout for joy.

The women called back and forth to each other as they hung damp clothes out to dry. The sailors sang as they hammered down the hatches and coiled ropes.

Even the animals seemed glad that the storm was over. Ducks and chickens quacked and clucked. Goats and sheep and pigs bleated and grunted in their pens on the forward deck.

Some of the boys were playing soldier on the main deck. Wrestling Brewster was the leader. He had often watched the men as they drilled every day under Captain Standish.

"Hold your gun higher, Love," he commanded his brother. The little boy shifted his stick higher on his shoulder.

"You had better wake up, John Billington," Wrestling called to a tall boy at the end of the line. "The Indians will surely get you if you don't."

"I'm awake," growled John. "Awake enough to smell dinner. Say, what is the matter with Constance Hopkins? Look at her." He pointed to a girl who ran toward them. Several of the smaller children followed her.

"Guess what has happened! Oh, guess!" she cried. "I have a new baby brother. He was born last night. Mother just let me hold him for a minute."

"A baby brother," said Love Brewster. "What is his name?"

"It's a funny name," answered Constance. "Mother is going to call him Oceanus because he was born on the ocean. My big brother Giles is making a cradle for him out of an empty case."

"Oceanus Hopkins," said Wrestling. "That is quite a name. Perhaps I can help Giles with the cradle or make a box to hold his clothes."

"Now there are four of us: Giles, Damaris, Oceanus, and me," said Constance. "Oh, Wrestling," she added, "I forgot to tell you that your mother said your dinner was ready. She says you must hurry for the food is hot this noon."

"Hurray! Come on, Love," said Wrestling. The two boys started off to find their mother.

Hot food was a real treat on the *Mayflower*. There were only two ways in which it could be cooked and both ways were hard. It could be put in a frying pan and held over a charcoal fire, or it could be cooked in a kettle hung on an iron tripod over a fire made in a box of sand.

Each day the food was taken from a common store and given out to the families. Even the smallest children knew that the food they carried on the boat must last them a long time. No one knew how long it might be before there would be any more.

Wrestling found his mother standing over a steaming kettle in the shelter of the cookhouse. She was dishing food into a wooden trencher.

"It is a good stew, my son," she said when she saw

Wrestling. "Dried beef, cabbage, turnips, and onions have gone into the making of it. After such terrible days of storm we all need something to make us strong. Take this for yourself and for Love." She held out a trencher filled with steaming stew.

"Thank you," said Wrestling. "It looks good and I am so hungry." He reached for the wooden dish.

"Wait," said his mother, setting the dish beside her. "I have just remembered the Hopkins children. With a new baby to care for, Mistress Hopkins will not be cooking for a few days. Go and get them, Wrestling. Ask them to share our dinner with us."

"May we eat out here on deck, Mother?" asked Love as Wrestling ran to get Giles and his sisters.

"Of course you may," said his mother. "And so will everyone else. It is so good to see the sun again."

In a few minutes the children sat together on the deck. Wrestling and Love dipped their spoons into the same trencher. Giles shared his with Constance and Mistress Brewster fed Damaris. There was little talking and a great deal of eating. Everyone was quite happy.

There were sunny days and stormy ones, but still the little *Mayflower* sailed the sea. Everyone was very tired of seeing nothing but water on all sides.

"We have been on this boat exactly sixty-three days," said Constance one afternoon. She and Giles were leaning against the railing watching the water.

"I know how long it is, because I counted this morning while I was waiting for everyone to wake up. I hate this boat. I hate living in that stuffy cabin with all those people. Sometimes I even hate Oceanus when he cries all night."

Wrestling, who stood nearby, sighed deeply. "Sometimes I don't believe we'll ever reach land," he said. "My mother said last night that she wished we were back in Holland."

"I don't," said Giles. "I want to fight the Indians and shoot tigers. The other day I heard two of the sailors talking about the Indians. They said that the Indians would eat us if they caught us. And they said—" Suddenly Giles stopped speaking. He looked carefully at the water for a minute. Then he pointed excitedly.

"Look!" he cried. "Do you see that?"

"What?" asked Constance. "Oh, that's only a dead tree branch. What do you care about that?"

"Silly!" said Giles. "Do trees grow in the ocean?"

"Look! Look! Come here," he called to some of the crew who were working nearby. The sailors dropped their work and ran to his side.

"There—a tree branch!" exclaimed Giles. "It means land is near, doesn't it?"

In a minute the deck was crowded with excited passengers. All were eager to see the first sign of land. Long after the tree branch had floated past them they talked about it.

"Watch for birds now," said one of the sailors. "If you see a wild duck or a goose you will know that we are really near the land."

So everyone who was able spent the rest of the day on deck. Each hoped to be the first one to sight land. But no one even saw a bird. At last it grew dark, and the children were sent below.

"Perhaps that branch came from a tree on an island and we have sailed past it," thought Constance sadly that night. She crawled into the bunk beside her little sister and was soon asleep.

But all night long on the boat men kept watch. Eyes peered eagerly into the darkness. There was much talk of what the next day would bring. Hearts were lighter, for surely now they were near their journey's end.

It was very early the next morning that the cry rang out, "Land ho! Land ho!" It woke all who were asleep in the cabin.

Men, women, and children rushed to the decks. The morning air was cold and they drew their cloaks about them. They peered into the distance.

Yes—there it was. At first it was only a dim shadow on the horizon. Then as the *Mayflower* sailed closer, rocks and trees appeared.

Everyone was excited. Everyone was happy. The children talked together and planned what they would do when they got off the boat.

But the sailors shook their heads. It was land—but it was not the end of their journey. They knew that the land they saw was Cape Cod. They were far north of the Hudson River, where they had planned to go.

So they turned the ship south and sailed along the coast. About noon they came to dangerous water. The breakers were so high that they were afraid the boat would be wrecked in them.

Then the captain and the men held a meeting and they decided to turn back to Cape Cod. All the afternoon they sailed north along the coast. When the children went to bed that night the ship was still moving through the water.

Early, early the next morning Giles woke and lay still for a moment wondering why he felt so queer. Suddenly he knew that the ship was not rushing through the water any longer.

He called Wrestling, and the two boys hurried to the deck. The *Mayflower* was at anchor in Cape Cod Bay.

How would you have felt if you had stood among the Pilgrims on the deck of the *Mayflower* that Saturday morning in November? Before them lay a strange land. No friends were there to welcome them. There were no houses to shelter them and no stores where they could buy their food.

When they looked toward the shore they could see only rocks, sand, and a forest of trees. Indians and wild beasts might be hiding there. It was winter, cold and stormy.

Yet no one said he was afraid. No one said he wanted to go back to his home in Holland or in England.

Together they kneeled on the deck and thanked God because He had brought them safely to this land, where they could live as they thought He wanted them to. Then they began to plan at once for their new homes. They were a brave people!

The Landing of the Pilgrim Fathers in New England

Felicia Hemans

The breaking waves dashed high
  On a stern and rock-bound coast,
And the woods against a stormy sky
  Their giant branches tossed;

And the heavy night hung dark
  The hills and waters o'er,
When a band of exiles moored their bark
  On the wild New England shore.

Not as the conqueror comes,
  They, the true-hearted, came;
Not with the roll of the stirring drums,
  And the trumpet that sings of fame;

Not as the flying come,
  In silence and in fear;—
They shook the depths of the desert gloom
  With their hymns of lofty cheer.

Amidst the storm they sang,
  And the stars heard, and the sea;
And the sounding aisles of the dim woods rang
  To the anthem of the free!

The ocean eagle soared
  From his nest by the white wave's foam;
And the rocking pines of the forest roared—
  This was their welcome home!

There were men with hoary hair
  Amidst that pilgrim band;—
Why had they come to wither there,
  Away from their childhood's land?

There was woman's fearless eye,
  Lit by her deep love's truth;
There was manhood's brow, serenely high,
  And the fiery heart of youth.

What sought they thus afar?—
  Bright jewels of the mine?
The wealth of seas, the spoils of war?
  They sought a faith's pure shrine!

Ay, call it holy ground,
  The soil where first they trod;
They have left unstained what there they found—
  Freedom to worship God.

The First New England Dinner

Maude R. Warren

It was almost twelve o'clock. Love and Bart were staggering down to the common house, each with a load of rushes. In the short morning there had been great progress in the building.

John Alden and Giles Hopkins had finished plastering the crevices between the logs with clay mortar. They were now working on the roof. Poles had been laid across it, and they were covering these with birch bark. On top of the birch bark would be bound the rushes which Bart and Love had been working so hard to gather.

Other men had marked out the lots on which the other houses were to be built. The men having the largest families were to have the largest plots. Bart Allerton's father had already set to work on his house, and Elder Brewster on his. It was thought that if each head of a family built his own house, the work would get on faster.

27

"Boys," John Alden called down, "you shall have a change of work now. Go back to the woods and bring all the chips and branches you can carry. We are going to have a fire."

"Good!" said Giles Hopkins. "That means hot food."

"We are to have the two wild ducks Captain Standish shot yesterday," John Alden said.

Love picked up an Indian basket that lay in a corner of the common house. He and Bart went back to the woods and began to gather branches and chips.

"Pick up pine cones, too," Love said, "for they burn well."

The boys gathered three loads of branches and three of chips before John Alden was satisfied. Then he said: "Why do you not set about building a fire? Love, go to your father, and ask him for his tinder box."

Love ran off and soon returned with a round box. Opening it, John Alden took out a flint, a steel, and a piece of linen which was called the tinder.

"Here, Bart," John said. "I have seen you strike fire from flint and steel."

Bart took the flint and steel and sat on the ground.

He struck the two together again and again, hoping that a spark would fall in the tinder and set it on fire. He knew, however, that it might be half an hour before he could make fire. Meanwhile, Love was shaving fine little slivers of wood from dry chips.

He added a few dry oak leaves, which he crumbled into a little dust heap. Then he sat watching Bart.

"Love," Giles Hopkins called, "John Alden says that we can cook our food, whatever it is, on the hearth."

The chimney of the common house was what is called a rung chimney. It was made of logs laid up crosswise, one upon another, and well plastered with clay, inside and out. The hearth was of hard-beaten clay. At the back, six feet from the floor, was the backlog in which two hooks had been set. That meant that two kettles of food could boil at the same time.

Bart was still working with flint and steel. Suddenly a little spark of fire fell on the linen.

"There!" cried Love. "You have struck a light at last."

They watched the linen slowly flame and scorch. Bart shaded it carefully with his hands until the tiny slivers of wood caught fire. Soon there was a blazing fire.

"We'll have to move it to the hearth on a shovel," Bart said.

John Alden climbed down from the roof of the common house.

"Out of my way, boys," he cried. "Let me pick up the fire."

He put the burning chips on a shovel and carried them into the common house. The boys followed him through the open door space. Some of the men stopped their work to watch John Alden building the first hearth fire ever made in the new home. Bart and Love added chips, and then boughs, to the growing fire.

Elder Brewster looked in as he was passing by.

"That is a cheerful sight," he said. "When we can

put a great log in that fireplace we shall know what comfort is."

"John Alden," Love cried, "where did the clay come from to chink the logs?"

"From the spring your father discovered—Pilgrim Spring," John replied. "You and Bart may go to the spring this moment. Take the big iron kettle which stands outside with our food. Fill it with water and bring it back."

The kettle weighed fully twenty pounds. Bart and Love carried it between them to the spring, which was a beautiful rivulet running down a slope. Blackberry and strawberry vines grew on the banks, and one or two willows drooped nearby. The boys knelt and drank. They thought they had never tasted more delicious water. Bart, who was very fond of his sisters, said, "I must carry some of this to Mary and Remember when we return to the *Mayflower*."

They filled the kettle and carried it back, stumbling a little under the weight. As they went on, they heard the sound of a shot. When they were near the common house they saw Captain Standish coming out of the wood. He carried his gun under his left arm and a great feathered creature in his right hand.

"Look men, all!" he shouted. "Our dinner will be the best you have tasted for many a day—if the lads show skill in cooking."

" 'Tis a wild turkey," said Giles Hopkins.

"Aye, and does not weigh less than twenty pounds, as

my good right arm can testify," said Miles Standish. "Here, boys, make the most of it. Let us see what cooks ye will prove."

The men smiled, but Bart, who felt that he was chief cook, looked very serious.

"Let Giles Hopkins hang the kettle on the chain and the chain on the hook of the backlog," he said. "I cannot lift so much alone."

Giles soon set the kettle swinging above the fire. The men went back to their work, while Bart took out his strong clasp knife.

"See, Love," he said. "I will cut off the two great wings. When they are dried we shall give them to our mothers to dust the hearth with."

"Perhaps they will serve as brooms, too," said Love.

"Not unless the women sweep on their knees," Bart said. "We shall find brooms in some way."

Bart had some difficulty in cutting off the wings of the turkey. Then he took off its head and feet.

"Now," he said to Love, "I shall dip it quickly in the hot water in the kettle, and then we'll take the feathers off."

As soon as the water was hot enough, Bart tied a piece of leather string around the legs of the turkey and dropped it in the water with a great splash. The hot water dashed over the hearth and spattered Love's doublet.

"Kettle is too full," said Bart. "Come and help me take him out."

They drew the turkey out and dropped it on the earth in front of the hearth. After a few moments they began to pick off the feathers. They did this rather awkwardly.

"Mother is quick at this," Bart said. "But she never let Mary or me help her, so I am slow."

"Should we not pour out this water and get clear?" asked Love.

"I suppose we should," said Bart, "but we have not time. The men will be hungry and will be sorry they trusted us if we wait much longer."

Bart cut open the turkey and drew it. Then he dipped out mugs of hot water and poured them on the turkey until it was thoroughly clean. Next he cut it up and dropped the pieces into the kettle.

"Here is the cover of the kettle," said Love.

Bart laughed.

"You don't think this is ready, do you?" he asked. "We must put salt in. And, oh, I have a good thought!"

He ran toward Giles Hopkins.

"Giles, will you give me the onions you were going to eat with your bread?" he asked.

"What do you want them for?" asked Giles. "Must I eat only dry bread?"

"Do but give them, Giles," Bart begged. "It is for the dish I am cooking."

"Take them, then," said Giles, good-naturedly. "I have them here in my doublet."

He handed Bart two large onions.

Bart took them, and he and Love cut them up quickly and dropped them into the kettle.

"Before many minutes now," said Bart proudly, "the men will be having the first hot meal in the common house."

Just before Bart thought the turkey was ready he said suddenly to Love: "But what will the men eat the broth in, Love? We have but two mugs here. I suppose they will have to take turns."

"No, they need not. You shall see!" cried Love. He ran down to the shore and before long came back with a pile of large clam shells.

"I saw these as we came up," he said. "They will hold many spoonfuls."

"Then we are all ready," said Bart. He called John Alden to lift the kettle off. The men stopped working on the roof and descended, calling to those who were working on the other houses. Love ran for the bread and sea biscuit, while John Alden lifted the kettle down upon the hearth. The men from outside entered, and all sat near the fire. Elder Brewster said a long grace. Then Bart and Love proudly dipped the two mugs into the kettle and poured into each clam shell a piece of turkey and some broth, and handed them to the men.

"Good!" cried Governor Carver and Miles Standish together, as they tasted the food. Elder Brewster and Mr. Allerton looked approvingly at their boys, but no one thought of praising them for what they had done.

And they expected no praise except the knowledge that they had carried out their work well.

Love thought he had never tasted anything better than his first fresh meat in Plymouth, and all the others enjoyed the meal.

Giles Hopkins loudly praised the flavor of his onions, while John Alden kept handing back his clam shell for more broth.

After dinner the boys listened to the men, who discussed further building. The houses well started were those of Governor Carver and Elder Brewster. They were to be built with the logs set horizontally and cemented with mud and clay. They might be roofed with logs, but only the governor's house was to have a puncheon floor.

"Puncheon floors are luxuries," said Elder Brewster. "Our gentle Mistress Carver must have one, but the rest of us must be content with the earth for a footing."

After they had rested sufficiently, the men went back to their work. The boys threw the refuse away and washed the pot and clam shells in cold sea water. Then they put the pot on one side of the hearth and the shells on the other.

They went to the woods next and carried away the broad strips of bark which Captain Miles Standish was cutting off the trees for roof building. Their bones and muscles ached, but they would not say they were tired. At about five o'clock the governor called to them.

"Come, lads," he said, "you have worked enough.

Giles Hopkins is going to the ship for blankets and other stores for those who will stay the night here. Go with him."

The boys were glad to go. They walked slowly after Giles to the shore and sat on the sand while he made signals to those on board to send the small boat. Soon two sailors rowed in to them, and they entered the boat, too tired to talk. They did not say anything until they reached the *Mayflower*. The little girls, Demaris Hopkins, Ellen More, and Mary Allerton, were leaning over the rail. Bart began to smile.

"We were doing their work today," he said. "I wonder if they could have made such good broth as ours."

As they climbed up the sides he called to Priscilla, who reached him her hand, "Oh, Priscilla, Love and I have just cooked the first New England dinner."

Then the women and children led the way to the cabin, and Bart and Love told all the events of their wonderful first day in Plymouth.

Indian Summer

Cornelia Meigs

The sun felt very pleasant as it lay across the tilted deck of the slow-sailing *Mary Belinda*. To Richard Fowler, sitting on the warm worn planks, it seemed as though he had spent a very large part of his ten years of life peering out under the great curve of the white mainsail, looking always toward the west.

There was fog beyond the nearest rolling waves this morning, a thin haze which was disappearing before the warm sun. And suddenly, as Dick was looking, the mist blew quite away and showed something that looked like a tiny, far-off picture, a green hill, a line of dark rocks at the foot of it and a white curl of breaking water.

He rubbed his eyes and looked again, out under the arch of the spreading sail. Could it be that the long journey was nearly ended? A second later the mist had shut down again. Not even the sailor on the lookout had been quick enough to see what Dick had seen. He was the first one on board to set eyes upon the long-watched-for land, the new wilderness country of America.

Richard had thought it a very wonderful and exciting thing when his father and mother, with a few brave-hearted friends, had packed up all their belongings and set out to find a new home in that country beyond the sea. Because they were all poor they had been able to hire no better ship than the slow, wide *Mary Belinda,* which had to carry a cargo first to the West Indies before it could bear them northward to the coast of New England.

It was late June when they set out, but now the length of the voyage had brought them into late October. Dick had heard his father saying very gravely that winter was no time to begin a settlement in a strange, cold country. Several of the others were complaining openly that they had all made a very serious mistake and that they must turn about and go home again.

Go home, after all this planning and journeying and looking forward to a new, free life! Dick felt that such a thing was not to be thought of for an instant.

The fog had lifted again, this time for a long space of several minutes, so that the lookout in his perch above sang out loudly, "Land ho!"

Everyone on board came hurrying to the rail, exclaiming, happy, almost unbelieving. The little picture of green shore and wooded hill appeared and disappeared as the wreaths of mist blew past, as though it were tantalizing them who wished so much to think that it was real, yet almost feared to do so. Dick, trying to get his father's attention as Master John Fowler stood talking to the captain, was obliged at last to touch him gently on the arm.

"When can I go ashore? You will surely let me go ashore, won't you?"

The captain answered instead of John Fowler.

"To be sure, boy, you shall go ashore. We've come to land somewhat north of where I intended. The colonies of Plymouth and Salem are a good many miles south, and this is a stretch of new country where you might find anything from wild apples to Indians. We won't go too far in toward land before tomorrow, since, if I'm not mistaken, we are going to have a bit of bad weather."

His sunburned face twinkled kindly as he looked down upon the boy, for Dick and the captain had become fast friends during the long voyage.

"Will it bring snow, do you think, Captain?" one of the women asked anxiously.

"It is only what you could expect at the end of October, madam," he replied gravely. "I have never come so far north as this coast of New England before; but even at home we look for dreary winter when bright October is gone."

Even as he spoke a chill breath of wind came stealing across the deck, making more than one person shiver under its cold, silent touch. A moment later the voice of the breeze grew shrill and loud and the ship began to stagger.

"Passengers below," shouted the captain, as he hurried

to his place in the stern and as the sailors began to swarm aloft to take in sail.

Next morning the wind was still hurrying and calling overhead and the deck was white with frozen snow. It had been a bitter night, breaking in cheerless gray when the morning came. There seemed no doubt that winter was upon them. A council of all the men in the company was being held in the cabin to discuss seriously the grave question of whether they should stay or return.

It took a bold heart, even at the best, to face the cold and dangers of planting a settlement in the wilderness. Would not the coming winter weather make even boldness of no use? Dick, passing the doorway, heard the captain speaking just inside.

"I do not make the winds, Master Fowler. I only do my best to carry folk across the sea by means of the breezes which Heaven sends us. I have found in my long life that we have to take the north winds as well as the south. You must even decide as best you can what is your wisest course. I will carry you back as safely as I brought you here, if that is your wish."

Dick's heart throbbed loudly as he heard. He could not go back, he could not bear it! If he had no more than a single day on that strange, exciting shore of America, even an hour, he would ask no more. But to put back without exploring a mile of it, that was not to be endured.

He climbed on deck and stood looking across the stretch of gray water. They were close to shore now, so that he could see the brown grass between the snow wreaths, the pointed, white-powdered pines and the curve of rocky shore with unbroken woods behind it. No one could deny that it looked forbidding in the cold, sunless morning light. The captain came to stand behind him.

"It may be that the whole company is going back without ever setting foot on land," he said. "But we will have to fill our water casks before the return voyage, so I am sending a boat to shore. If you are of mind to go with it, drop over the rail when the men are ready. But do not blame me if you find the expedition a bitter cold one."

The rocky shore, as they came rowing to it across the heaving waters, was broken by the mouth of a little creek. It made a sandy bay where the big breakers flattened out into long, easy billows. Here the sailors beached the boat, lifted out the water casks, and began looking about for a spring or a pond of fresh water.

It was Dick who clambered over the outcropping rocks and came upon a little lake, a pocket among the granite boulders, full and clear with sweet, fresh water. He would have helped with the filling of the water barrels but the boatswain said that was too heavy a task for a boy.

"Go and explore a little farther, if you've a mind to," the man suggested. "We have to row these casks back to the ship and get another boatload, so that you can spend a good two hours anyway here on land. I don't believe there's another of the shipload of passengers will want to put a foot on this shore. The sight of the snow and ice has seemed to take the heart out of the whole company of them."

It was welcome permission to Dick, who was longing to see what sort of a strange country this America might be. He was off at once, up the hillside and along the ridge where the pine trees stood so tall and close. He had never felt just such a sharp, keen wind as this which blew in his face off the snow-capped hills, never known such a springy feeling as that of the snow and the pine needles under his tramping feet.

He climbed one hill, then another, stopped to look at the tracks of small-footed animals, turned aside to pick some bright red berries showing through the snow. He jumped back when a brown bird rose from almost between his feet with a loud whirring of wings. He trudged gaily on, not knowing how far he had got from the beach, not understanding at all that he was lost.

His first faint thought that he should be turning back brought him in a flash the knowledge that he did not know the right direction. He looked all about him at the hills and the crowded trees, with no glimpse anywhere of the gray expanse of the sea.

He might have been bewildered and frightened had not something caught his eye at that moment and turned his attention completely from the idea of returning to the boat. It was the sight of a drift of smoke going up among the bushes not a hundred yards away.

He ran toward it quickly, burst through a thicket, and stood at the edge of a clearing, breathless and full of wonder. A boy and a girl of about his own age were kneeling before the mouth of a great hollow log from which the smoke was curling upward. At the first snap of a twig under his foot the boy jumped up, while both turned about to stare at him. Not until he saw their brown, clean-cut faces did he have the least idea that here were Indians.

They stood looking at one another, the white boy and the two young red-skinned Americans. It would have been hard to tell which was the most surprised. The Indian lad, who was taller than Dick, flashed him a sudden hostile look and slipped his hand to his hunting knife. But the girl, saying something in their own language, went on with the task at which they had been busy, that of stuffing great handfuls of the deep, wet moss into the opening of the hollow log.

With the quickness of an alert boy's wit Dick understood what they were about. They had made a fire in the mouth of the log, perhaps to smoke out some small animal which had taken refuge there.

Now the blaze was getting beyond their control and they were trying to put it out. The long, soft moss grew everywhere and, wet with snow as it was, served almost as well as water for fighting the blaze which flashed back from the dark hole and could be heard crackling deep within the dry heart of the dead tree.

The green pines stood everywhere, full of pitchy sap, fine fuel for the leaping flames should they once escape into the woods. Dick knew nothing of forest fires, but he could see that these two were working as though for their very lives.

In an instant he was across the clearing and had knelt down to help them. He snatched a great handful of the moss and thrust it into the hot opening, feeling a breath of fire scorch his cheek as he did so. The Indian boy brushed against his shoulder as he stooped to push his own armload down the throat of the blazing log.

There must have been a hollow through the whole length of the fallen tree, as far as the small end buried among the bushes. The draught fed the fire so that it snapped and crackled and reached out in long, wicked tongues of flame, so that the three fighters had to jump back again and again.

Yet each time one or another would fill his arms with the wet green stuff and, watching his chance, would press it into place and smother the blaze for a minute. The Indian boy would have his turn, then Dick, then the girl, then the brown boy again.

They had pulled up all the moss nearby and had to run, panting, farther and farther afield to gather more. Two people could never have worked fast enough to keep ahead of the fire. But with three the battle began, at last, to go against the stubborn blaze. It choked, threw out clouds of smoke, burst out again, and finally died down to a faint glow.

The Indian boy stood back, a smile of triumphant satisfaction on his face. But the girl cried out suddenly in warning and caught Dick's arm to thrust him aside.

There was a sound of struggling deep within the log, and a big, dark shape pushed out through the charred opening. A black, furry bear, looking enormous in the whirl of smoke, coughing and grunting in discomfort and displeasure, scrambled hastily over the coals. He

stood still a moment on the grass to shake off the cinders which clung, glowing, to his deep coat.

Then the big beast went shambling off into the forest, evidently too bewildered by the strange disturbance to feel like stopping to reckon with those who had brought it about. All three stood watching, open-mouthed, as the animal went crashing off through the underbrush and disappeared.

The boy moved first. He looked at the girl and jerked his head in the direction where their village must lie. His grin seemed to mean that they had done well to escape the punishment which would have fallen upon them had the fire spread to drive their people from the camp. Then he swung about to face Dick and spoke a word which the white boy could understand.

"English?" he asked.

Evidently both of these two had traveled southward for fishing or trading and had come into some contact with the settlements at Plymouth and Salem. Between them they could muster several words and seemed to take in what Dick tried to say in reply.

The girl, as she nodded and smiled, brought out a package of dried deer meat and a bark cup of berries, which she laid out along the top of the half-burned log. Dick became suddenly aware of how long he had been tramping and how hungry he was. He scarcely needed the girl's sign of invitation before he sat down between the two and began to eat.

They managed to talk together, somehow, with signs and such few words of English as the Indian pair could understand. Dick learned where their camp was, what sort of hunting they had during the summer, how many warriors mustered about the fires at night. Would the white men, the two asked, would the strangers make a camp for themselves on the shore to which the ship had come?

"No," Dick answered. His face fell suddenly as he remembered that which he had almost forgotten, the council on the ship and the probable plan to go back to England. He tried to explain, clumsily, how they had been so long in coming that now, since the winter was here, they would have to give up their great purpose and go back again.

The Indian boy, when at last he understood, looked at him long and steadily. Then he spoke three English words, easy to comprehend, but astonishing in their meaning.

"Summer comes again," he said.

That was true, Dick agreed, but made a sign with his hands to mean that a very long time must pass before there would be summer once more. But the other boy shook his head with energy. He held up three fingers, then five. He seemed to be trying to say that in three days, or at most five, it would be summer again.

The girl joined in with clever, vivid signs to make Dick see the truth, that here in America there was another summer, a little one, but warm and gentle and hazy, the last beautiful weather before the deep snows buried the hills.

Dick sat staring at them, not believing, for a long

minute. Then, really taking in what they said, he suddenly jumped up without a further word and ran, stumbling and noisy, away through the wood.

The Indian boy, when he spoke of the ship, had pointed in the direction where she lay. It was Dick's only means of knowing which way to go, but he followed it, breathless and hasty, without even looking back. Half a mile from the beach he met the party of sailors who, after long waiting and grumbling, had come to look for him.

The council in the cabin was still sitting, for the question of whether to go or stay could not be decided. Most of the company wished to go back; only a few of the bolder souls were still not quite willing to agree. At last Master John Fowler pushed his chair back with a sigh.

"I fear we must give up all of our great hopes," he said. "A single month of good weather would have given us time to make some shelter for ourselves, but with the winter really here—"

He was interrupted by a disturbance outside, by rapid feet coming down the ladder, and by the bursting open of the door to admit a wind-blown boy in wild haste.

"It is not really winter," Dick cried out to them. "The Indians say that this is not winter, that the summer comes again."

It was a little more than a year later that the small settlement beside the bay was celebrating its first harvest. The Indians had been friendly; the meadows between the outcropping rocks proved fertile; the colony felt itself safe and well established now. That short season, which they had come to speak of as the Indians' summer, had given them time to make themselves secure against the cold weather.

And now that the harvest was safe they had adopted the same plan as the other colonies to the south of them, and were giving up a day to thanksgiving for the mercy of God who had so prospered their undertaking. It was very cold on that November day, with a deep snow which had fallen the night before. But smoke was going up from every stone chimney to show how the good wives were making preparation for a bountiful meal.

There was one, however, who did not eat at any board of feasting that day. As the sun rose toward noon, Dick Fowler turned his back on the bustle of making ready and took his way alone to the hills. He had put a loaf of bread into his pocket and a handful of corn. He stopped when he came to a certain clearing, where a big log, still showing the marks of a burned-out fire, lay nearly buried in the snow.

He waited, but not for long. It was even as he hoped, for two quick figures came silently out of the wood to stand beside him.

These three friends, with a meal of dried venison, bread, and corn laid out upon the rough bark, sat down to eat Thanksgiving dinner of a strange sort there within the circle of the snow-crowned pines.

Indians for Thanksgiving

Dorothy Heiderstadt

It was Thanksgiving Day in New England in 1631.

Betsy and her sister Prudence had been left at home while their father and mother went to church. The girls had wanted to go along, but their parents thought the snow was too deep.

"Be good," said their father as he shouldered his gun and opened the door. "Keep the fire going and the turkey basting, and keep the doors shut."

The doors had to be kept shut and bolted for the same reason their father had to carry a gun all the time. Indians lurked in the forest—Indians with painted faces, bows and arrows and tomahawks.

Betsy and Prudence had never seen any of the enemy Indians. The only Indians they knew were Red Squirrel and the people of his tribe, who lived back in the forest and were friendly to the white people. But Red Squirrel and the other friendly Indians had moved away almost a year ago, and since then only the white people had lived in the forest.

Betsy and Prudence lived in a log cabin on the edge of the forest. Through the forest ran a path, and at the end of this path, about three miles away, was the church where their father and mother were going.

The two children peered through the window and watched their parents going down the path—their father dressed in his black suit with the wide white collar and the wide white cuffs, with his tall hat on his head, his silver-buckled shoes on his feet, and his long gun on his shoulder; their mother in her gray cloak lined with blue, with the shirt of her long gray dress showing beneath, her little gray cap on her head, and her Bible in her hand. If you have ever seen any pictures of Pilgrims going to church you will know exactly how Betsy's and Prudence's father and mother looked that day.

Betsy sighed as she watched them go.

"I wish I could have gone along," she said. "Maybe I would have seen an Indian."

"Betsy!" said Prudence in a shocked voice. She frowned sternly at her sister, who was a year younger than she. "You wouldn't want to see an Indian. The only ones you would be likely to see in this forest would be the kind that come with tomahawks!"

"Red Squirrel wasn't that kind," protested Betsy.

"There aren't many Indians like Red Squirrel," said Prudence. "Come on. I'm going to baste the turkey, and you'll have to help hold the saucepan."

The turkey was roasting on a long pole set across the fireplace, just over the fire. While Betsy held the long-handled saucepan beneath the turkey, Prudence poured spoonfuls of water from the saucepan onto it. This kept the meat from becoming too dry as it roasted.

By and by, when the turkey had been basted enough, Betsy put down the saucepan and went back to the window to look out. The forest lay cold and still in the gray light of the winter morning. The trees were black and bare. The ground was covered with snow, and the snow was covered with little tracks made by rabbits and squirrels. Betsy looked at the forest and went on thinking about Indians.

"Just the same, I would like to see an Indian. Not a big one," she went on hastily. "Just a little one would do. One of Red Squirrel's children."

"Betsy," called Prudence from her chair beside the fire, "what are you talking to yourself about? Come away from that cold window. Let's throw pine cones onto the fire. You like to do that, don't you?"

"Yes," said Betsy reluctantly, moving away from the window. It was fun to throw pine cones onto the fire. They blazed up beautifully. She was quite happy for a while, and she forgot about Red Squirrel's children, whom she missed a great deal. Since they had moved away, she had no other children to play with. Prudence, who was ten, was quite grown up and liked to bake and knit, and refused to play with dolls any more. The children of the other white people in the forest lived too far away.

Anyhow, nobody, in Betsy's opinion, was as much fun as an Indian child to play with. Indian children knew such lively games and they wore such lovely beads. It was not long before she began to grow tired of the pine cones and to think about Indians again.

Prudence was knitting a muffler for her father. Her knitting needles clicked industriously, and Betsy felt somewhat uneasy as she watched her work. Soon she would have to learn to knit. The thought was almost insufferable. She was sure that she could never learn to do it as it ought to be done.

"Dear me!" said Prudence suddenly, looking at the fire. "We need some more wood. I'll have to go out into the storeroom and get some."

She laid aside her knitting and arose. The storeroom had been built onto the back of the house. In it were piles of wood, pumpkins, potatoes, and apples; dried herbs hung down from the ceiling. A door opened into it from the room where the children were.

"Want me to help you?" asked Betsy, jumping up eagerly.

"No," said Prudence. "Stay in here by the fire. You know it's cold out there, and you aren't over your cold yet."

Betsy sighed and wandered over to the window. The morning seemed very long. The good smell of roast turkey filled the room, and her mouth watered. Two hours until dinnertime! How could she wait? If she could only have some of it now! If she could only see an Indian!

Suddenly she gasped. Her eyes, which had been wan-

dering aimlessly over the forest, stared at something—
something that was moving out there among the trees,
something quite small and close to the ground. It looked
like a little boy.

"Prudence!" cried Betsy excitedly. "Look! Look! An
Indian!"

Prudence dropped her wood with a clatter and flew to
the window. "Where? Where?" she gasped, turning pale.
Visions of tomahawks and war paint ran through her
head.

"There! See?" whispered Betsy, pointing. And just at
that moment there emerged from the forest a little Indian boy, all alone. He was about five years old, and he
had a little round, fat face and two bright black eyes. He
was wrapped in a bright blanket, and he was floundering
valiantly through the snow toward the house.

"It must be one of Red Squirrel's children!" cried
Prudence. "That means Red Squirrel has come back."

But Betsy was scornful. "Of course, that isn't any of
Red Squirrel's children," she announced. "Don't I know
exactly what every one of them looks like? This is a
strange Indian. Oh, look at him, Prudence! Isn't he
cunning?"

The little Indian was standing within a few feet of
the door, staring around him curiously and stamping the
snow off his moccasined feet.

"Let's get him to come in!" whispered Betsy. "Maybe
he's lost. Maybe he's hungry." Her eyes grew large and
dark with sympathy at the thought. Was not she herself

actually suffering for a taste of that turkey roasting over the fire?

Prudence, meanwhile, had gone to the door and opened it.

"Do come in!" she said politely to the small Indian. "I'm sure you must be cold out there."

"Oh, Prudence!" Betsy laughed, running over to stand beside her. "He doesn't understand what we say."

They flung the door wide open, and beckoned to the little Indian. He looked at them solemnly for a moment. Perhaps he had never before seen two such little girls in long gray dresses, white aprons, and buckled shoes. Perhaps he had never seen a house before. At any rate, he remained standing there staring, first at them and then at the house.

Then, just as they were beginning to get cold, and to wonder what to do next, he walked gravely past them into the house. Once there he continued to look curiously all around him—at the ceiling of the room, at the chairs, the table, the spinning wheel, and the fireplace.

At sight of the fireplace, his eyes sparkled. He went close to the fire and held out his hands to it. He sniffed the air hungrily, and Betsy, watching him, felt a pang of hunger, too.

"I believe he's hungry," said Prudence. "We must give him something to eat."

"Perhaps we ought to eat with him," suggested Betsy quickly, "so he won't feel impolite to be eating there in front of us."

"And leave Father and Mother to eat their Thanksgiving dinner alone?" demanded Prudence in a shocked voice.

"That's right. We couldn't do it," said Betsy with a sigh.

The table was already set for dinner, although it would still be quite a while before their father and mother would be home.

Prudence and Betsy carved a piece very carefully off the turkey, and put it on a plate. They put a big spoonful of sauce beside it and one of potatoes and gravy. Then they helped the little Indian off with his blanket, and put him in front of the table in a chair.

All this time the little Indian had not said one word. He allowed them to lift him into his chair. But he looked uncertainly at the food on his plate. He picked up the turkey in his hands, hesitantly, and took a bite. Then he laid it down and put out a hand to pick up the potatoes and gravy the same way.

"Wait!" cried Prudence, and he drew back his hand quickly. "He doesn't know how to eat. We'll have to feed him."

So they each got a spoon and took turns feeding the little Indian. First Prudence would put a spoonful of potatoes and gravy into his mouth. Then when he had swallowed that Betsy would put in a spoonful of sauce. Then the little Indian would take a bite of turkey, and then a bite of bread. They made a game out of it, and presently the little Indian was laughing so much that he could scarcely eat.

Suddenly, in the midst of the game, he looked at the window and gave a pleased, excited cry. He pointed toward the window and began to talk very fast in his own language. He struggled to get down out of his chair.

Betsy and Prudence, somewhat surprised, helped him down and followed him over to the window. He peered out of it eagerly, talking all the while. He kept looking up at them to see whether they understood. He even grew a little impatient with them because they could not understand. They, too, looked out of the window, but there was nothing in sight.

Outside, the snow was falling fast, and so thick were the flakes that the children could see only to the first trees of the forest. All the little rabbit and squirrel tracks were being rapidly filled.

Looking at the little Indian, Prudence wondered uneasily what he had seen through the window. Suppose an Indian had looked in—a wild, savage Indian, the kind who carried a tomahawk! Suppose this was the child of that sort of an Indian! She began to wish that her parents would hurry home.

The little Indian, however, shrugged his shoulders at last and returned to his interrupted meal. When he had eaten everything on his plate, his head suddenly began to nod and he leaned against Prudence's shoulder.

"He's sleepy. Let's carry him over to the old settle by the fire," whispered Prudence. So with much careful tugging and pulling, the two children managed to carry their guest over to the old settle. He slept peacefully. After clearing away his place at the table, Prudence and

Betsy returned to the fire, and sat down beside it. Prudence threw some more sticks on it, and then took up her knitting. Betsy, on a low footstool quite close to the old settle, looked at the little Indian.

"Isn't he nice?" she whispered to Prudence. "His tribe must be camping here in the forest, and I suppose he wandered off and got lost. I imagine his mother is worried about him, don't you? He's such a little boy."

"I don't know, I'm sure," said Prudence, counting stitches primly. "I only hope that when they find him here they won't think we were trying to steal him, and tear the house down over our heads."

Betsy put out a hand and touched the hand of the little Indian. "They won't do that," she said softly. "He will tell them that we are his friends, and that we gave him part of our Thanksgiving dinner."

"I hope so," said Prudence shortly, going on with her stitches.

Betsy leaned drowsily against the settle and looked into the fire.

"I hope he's going to live here in the forest," she said. "Then we can play with him, and we won't miss Red Squirrel's children so. I've missed them dreadfully."

"And a good thing they went away," said Prudence. "A great girl like you, who should have learned to knit and bake long ago, playing around with Indians!"

But she smiled at her small sister as she said this, and Betsy, who had long since learned that Prudence was not so stern as she sounded, smiled back at her.

"Dear me!" said Prudence suddenly. "I'm a little tired of knitting, myself, right now. I guess everything's ready for dinner. The turkey is in the covered dish close to the fire where it will keep warm. I think I'll rest awhile." And she drew her own footstool up close to the settle, and leaned against it as Betsy was doing.

So warm was the room, so drowsy was the sound of the fire purring and crackling on the hearth, that in a few minutes both the children were fast asleep.

This was really too bad, for if Betsy had only remained awake five minutes longer, she would have seen an Indian, such as she had hoped to see if she had gone to church. An Indian was looking in at the window!

Betsy's father and mother, coming down the forest path, were not pleased when they saw several Indians looking in at their front window. In fact, they were badly frightened.

The father shifted his gun under his arm and started forward quickly.

"Wait!" said his wife in a low voice. "Let us see if they are friendly. Speak to them first!"

At the sound of her voice, one of the Indians turned quickly, and the father, much to his relief, recognized the face of Red Squirrel, the friendly Indian, who had moved away.

The other Indians turned around, too. Red Squirrel spoke to them quietly. Then he came forward to greet his friends, the two white people. Silently he made signs for them to come and look in at the window, too.

Wondering, they did so. Inside the big room they saw the fire burning on the hearth, the kettle steaming cheerfully, and the table set for Thanksgiving. They saw their children fast asleep beside the settle. They saw the little Indian stretched out comfortably on top of the settle.

One of the strange Indians, who was wearing a large and imposing feather war bonnet, began to talk very fast. He talked for quite a long time, and then stopped suddenly and stood looking at Betsy's and Prudence's father and mother, with snapping black eyes as though waiting.

"He says," began Red Squirrel, "that he is White Bear, who rules a powerful tribe of the Pequot Indians. This morning the braves in his tribe were to go on the warpath against the white people who live in this forest. As they were leaving, it was discovered that the son of the chief was gone. He had wandered away into the forest. Then this big snow began to fall, and they were afraid that they might not find him again.

"One of them heard the sound of children laughing in this cabin, and looked in at this window. There he saw the chief's son eating at your table. He ran and told the chief.

"Do you understand what your children have done? They have taken in a child of their enemies and warmed him at their fire. He was hungry, and they fed him. He says that he, White Bear, will not forget this. From this day he will be the friend of the white people of this forest just as I am your friend.

"When I heard that he was coming here to make war

on the white people, I came as quickly as I could to see if I could not persuade him to stop. Now it is not necessary. Your children have persuaded him because they have been kind to his son."

When Red Squirrel had finished speaking the white man held out his hand.

"Come in, all of you," he said, "and share our Thanksgiving dinner."

So the Indians went in, with great dignity, to share the Thanksgiving dinner. Betsy, who was the first of the children to awake, was at first terrified and then delighted when she saw all the Indians. Even Prudence was somewhat thrilled over sitting down to dinner with a real Indian chief who wore such an imposing war bonnet.

He did not wear the war bonnet during the meal, however. Red Squirrel persuaded him to take it off.

The little Indian boy, whose name, by the way, was Little Wolf, was delighted to see his father. Although he had already been given one Thanksgiving dinner, he found that he was able to eat another.

Poor Betsy, who had been so hungry a little while before, was now so busy staring at the Indians and asking Red Squirrel about his children that she very nearly forgot to eat. After that day she had a wonderful time with twice as many Indian children to play with as she had had before. She had the children of Red Squirrel's tribe and the children of White Bear's tribe, too. Her mother despaired of ever getting her to learn to bake and knit.

As for the Indians, they were the friends of the white

people always, just as they had promised they would be. The powerful tribe of White Bear lived nearby in the forest for many years. In the winter Betsy's and Prudence's mother often found wild game or deer meat outside her door, left there for her by the Indian hunters. And every Thanksgiving Day White Bear and Little Wolf and Red Squirrel and several other Indians came to Betsy's and Prudence's house for dinner.

The story of how peace was first made between the tribe of White Bear and the white people in that New England forest became as popular as a fairy tale or a legend. It was told around Indian campfires at night. It was told by white grandmothers to their grandchildren. And from that day on that peace was kept forever and ever.

The Black Sheep's Coat
Cornelia Meigs

The orange-red beam of light from the swinging ship's lantern dipped and swayed from side to side of the narrow cabin. It showed the red coat of the soldier who sat at the table; it lit the pale face of Peter Perkins, the stoop-shouldered clerk; it shone on Granny Fletcher's clicking knitting needles, and, in a far corner, it dropped across the white paper upon which Master John Carver's goose-quill pen was moving so busily.

Once in a while, at long intervals, the light swung so far with the plunging of the ship that it penetrated even the cranny behind the big beam where Andrew Newell was crouching, with his knees doubled up to his chin and his head bowed, to keep out of sight in the shadow.

"One more dip like that," the boy was thinking desperately, as the exploring ray seemed to seek him out of fell purpose, "and the whole company will see me. How will it fare with me then, I wonder? Will they cast me overboard?"

So far, however, the little company was quite unconscious of his presence. Master Carver laid down his pen and began to read aloud in a low voice to the two men who sat near him, David Kritchell and William Bradford.

The hidden boy could not see the first two, but he had a full view of William Bradford who sat beyond, a young man with broad, square shoulders where the others had the stoop of scholars and clerks, whose open brow and clear, merry eyes were in contrast to the serious and stern faces of his companions.

"This *Mayflower* is a rolling ship," complained the old woman who was knitting; "it has tumbled my ball of yarn out of my lap so many times that I will even let it go where it wills for a while."

The gray ball, slowly unwinding, rolled across the cabin toward Andrew's hiding place, but for the space of a few minutes no one noticed it. The soldier had reached the climax of the story of one of his campaigns.

"I drew my sword," he was saying, "but there were five cutthroat Spaniards all rushing upon me at once. I struck—"

"When last you told us that tale, Captain Standish, you made it only four," Granny Fletcher interrupted tartly, "three big ones and a little one; and the time before—"

"Never mind the other times, woman," returned

Standish testily. The lurching of the ship had spilled the ashes from his pipe, serving to irritate him still more, so that he added savagely, "We will all have tales to tell soon, I will wager, of Indians that burn and scalp and slay every Christian that they see."

"Heaven have mercy!" cried the granny, casting up her eyes. "Such dangers as lie before us! Perhaps those who turned back on the *Speedwell* did wisely, after all. Where is my ball of yarn?"

It was very near to Andrew, but the name of the *Speedwell* had made him wince and draw himself closer into his corner. It was on that very ship that he should have been sailing back to England, as he well knew.

His uncle, the only relative he had in the world and no very kindly one at that, had agreed to take the boy with him on this great adventure of planting a Puritan colony in the New World. But with the first day of the voyage, the worthy man's ardor had cooled and he had been glad enough to avail himself of the chance of return when the leaky *Speedwell* turned back.

A hasty council had been held in the *Mayflower's* cabin as to who should go on and who should be carried back to England, at which gathering Andrew, in spite of his uncle's protests, had pushed into the front rank of those who wished to go forward.

"We are already overcrowded, and it is the able-bodied men that we need," John Carver had said.

"And those who will make solid and worthy citizens," Peter Perkins had added at his elbow, with an unfriendly glance at Andrew's shabby coat. William Bradford was the only one who had looked at him kindly, and even he had shaken his head.

"It is a great enterprise," he said, "but we must needs abide by the rule of the elders as to who is to go and who must return."

That shabby coat was now the worse for a great rent in the shoulder and a smear of tar on the sleeve, put there when Andrew had squeezed into a narrow hiding place between two great coils of rope, instead of entering the crowded boat that put off for the other vessel. For a whole day of light winds he had waited in an agony of suspense, while they lay close to the *Speedwell,* never seeming to get so far away that he was safe from being returned to her.

Toward evening, however, the breeze freshened, the two ships had drawn apart, and while the whole company was gathered in the bow to see the last of their companion vessel, Andrew had slipped below to hide in some better place than on the wet open deck of the *Mayflower.*

A footstep in the passage had alarmed him so that he had dashed into the main cabin and crawled behind a beam, for want of a better refuge. Here he still lurked, cramped, aching, and hungry, wondering how soon the lantern or the ball of yarn would be the means of betraying him.

Just as he felt sure that Granny Fletcher's sharp eye must have caught sight of his protruding elbow there came a diversion in the sound of scurrying feet on the companionway and in the headlong entry of two excited girls, one about fourteen years old, the other twelve.

"Oh, Father," cried the elder one, seizing David Kritchell's arm, "one of the sailors just helped me to climb up to look into the pen where the sheep and the poultry are, and what do you think! There is a little new lamb among them, not more than a day old!"

"Nay, my dear Drusilla," her father remonstrated, "do you not see that this is no time to speak of such matters? You are interrupting Master Carver."

"There is no harm wrought," John Carver said; "she brings good news, for surely it promises well that our flocks should already begin to increase."

"But it is a—a black sheep," Drusilla declared. "You cannot think how strange it looks among the white ones!"

"A black sheep?" cried Granny Fletcher in shrill consternation. "There is a sign of bad luck, indeed! It is enough to send us all to the bottom. A black cat's crossing our path could not be a worse omen."

"We are scarcely in danger from the passing of any black cats," William Bradford observed, with twinkling eyes. "As for the black lamb, it shall be your very own, Mistress Drusilla, since it was you who brought us tidings of it. I think this expedition of ours is too earnest and weighty an affair to be brought to ruin by one black sheep."

"Nay, nay, we are as good as lost already," wailed the granny, so voluble in her lamenting that John Carver was forced to tell her sternly to hold her peace.

"Cobwebs and moonshine!" exclaimed Miles Standish, filling up his pipe. "There are enough straight swords and ready muskets in this company to drive away any sort of bad luck."

Granny Fletcher, much subdued, got up to fetch her yarn, which still rolled back and forth at the far end of the cabin. The crouching boy held his breath as it moved first toward him, then away, and then, with a sudden plunge of the ship, tumbled directly into his lap, so that he and the old woman stooping to grasp it were brought face to face. The poor soul's nerves were too badly shaken to withstand the shock of seeing that unexpected, tar-streaked countenance so close to her own.

"The bogyman, the evil one himself come to destroy us all!" she screamed in such terror that all in the cabin rose to their feet.

"Come forth, whoever is there," commanded Bradford sternly.

It was in such manner that Andrew Newell, gentleman adventurer at the age of fifteen, made his appearance as a member of the company of the Pilgrim Fathers.

There followed an uproar of questions, reproaches, and rebukes, with Granny Fletcher's shrill scolding rising high above all the rest, until John Carver struck his hand upon the table for silence.

"We must not talk of what the boy has done, but of what we are to do with him," he began. "He is among us, without friends—"

"And without money to pay his passage, I'll be bound," observed Peter Perkins in an undertone. "Look at his coat; look at his dirty face! This is no company for waifs and ragamuffins. Born to die on the gallows, that is the sort he is!"

The Pilgrims, while few of them were rich, were nearly all of that thrifty class which had little patience with careless poverty. In their eyes Andrew's ragged coat was less to be forgiven than his uninvited appearance among them.

Drusilla was tugging at her father's elbow. "Think how much he wanted to come, to dare all this for the sake of seeing the New World," she whispered.

"It is not zeal for our faith that has led him," said Peter Perkins, overhearing her, "but mere love of adventure."

"And is love of adventure so wicked a thing?" questioned Bradford, his deep, quiet voice overriding all the buzz of excited talk. "I can understand why the boy wished to go with us and I will be responsible for him. You have, many of you, brought servants, bound to you to repay their passage by a year or two years of labor. This lad shall be bound to me in the same way and I will stand surety for him. Do you agree?" he said to Andrew. "Will you serve me?"

Did he agree! Andrew felt, as he crossed the cabin to his supporter's side, that he would die for this young elder who stood among his gray-haired seniors and gave the boy the only friendly smile in all that hostile company.

"He will bring us ill luck," he heard Granny Fletcher

whisper to her neighbor. "Is not one black sheep enough for our voyage?"

"Born to die on the gallows, I know the look of them," Peter Perkins returned, wagging his head.

Through the long days of the voyage that followed, those two seemed like watchful, sharp-tongued ghosts that haunted Andrew's footsteps. Whatever went amiss, they laid the blame upon him, whatever he did was bound, in their eyes, to be wrong.

"There are always scolds in every company," Bradford told him one day, when the reproaches of his two enemies seemed past bearing. "Whether such persons wear breeches or petticoats, they are just the same, and real men must learn to close their ears to them."

Day by day Andrew grew to admire ever more this man who had befriended him. Bradford's kindliness, his good sense, and the steady burning of the fire of his enthusiasm made him stand out from all the rest, since amid the depression and the deadly weariness of the long voyage he was ever cheerful, confident, and certain of their success.

"I was only of your age when I first joined the company of the dissenters myself," he told Andrew once, "and I looked with all a boy's wonder on the ups and downs, the bickerings and complaints, the discouragements of their venture in establishing a church and in making their pilgrimage to Holland. But now I can see that it was mere human nature, and that there is real patience and courage in the heart of every one of them."

Hostility toward Andrew abated somewhat during the voyage, although, to the end, Bradford, Carver, David Kritchell, and his two daughters were the only ones who treated him with any real kindness. And that voyage, even as Bradford was always prophesying, came to an end suddenly just when they were beginning to feel that life on the high seas must last forever.

Andrew and Drusilla had gone on deck before the others one chill early morning in November, a morning of light winds from the west, with the wide sea still stretching endlessly all about them.

Then, "Oh, Andrew!" "Oh, Mistress Drusilla!" each cried to the other in the same breath, for each had perceived the same thing. The sharp odor of salt spray, the sting of the sea wind, had altered strangely; there came instead warm puffs of air across the water, while a line like a dark cloud stretched along the horizon. They had reached America at last!

That going ashore—how they had dreamed of it, and how unlike it was to what they had thought! They were used to a land that was green through most of the winter, so that they looked with dismay at the brown, bare woods, the unfamiliar somber green of the pines, and the line of rolling hills in the distance.

They coasted along the shore for days, finally choosing an abiding place merely because winter was coming close and some decision must be made. The men who landed first reported that there was high open ground, a cheerful, chattering stream of fresh water, and a good prospect over both sea and land.

"We also caught sight of four Indians and a dog," Captain Standish said, "but they stayed not for our coming and stopped only to whistle to their beast before they ran away. Yet we thought we saw them later, peeping and peering among the forest trees."

The next morning they went ashore all together, with bags and bundles and precious possessions, with the swine and the poultry and the bleating sheep from the pen amidships. Drusilla Kritchell could scarcely be separated from her beloved black lamb, but Andrew, who was to go in the boat with such of the livestock as could not swim, promised that he would take good care of it.

"And a fine pair they will make, the two black sheep of ill omen," remarked Peter Perkins, who, amid all the bustle of landing, could still find time for a bitter word.

"A goodly place," said David Kritchell cheerily as they stood on the beach surveying their new home and waiting for the last of their gear to be landed. The thin sunshine lay upon the flat, wet shore and the chill wind seemed to search out the very marrow of the travelers' bones. The cries of the gulls circling above them sounded harsh and lonely. The last of the boats grated its keel on the gravel and the whole company turned their faces toward the hill. Suddenly Granny Fletcher, half-hysterical, threw up her hands and lifted her voice in a long wail.

"We will perish here in this wilderness!" she cried. "God meant us to endure our persecutions in patience at home and not flee from them to a land where wild beasts and savages will soon make an end of us. What

will we eat? Where will we lay our heads? Oh, England
—England——!"

Her cry died away in choking sobs, while the others
looked at one another. The *Mayflower* rode in the tide-
way, her sails, wet from last night's rain, all spread to
dry, white and shining in the sun. The very wind that
filled them blew full and fresh toward home. Yet, to the
everlasting honor of the Pilgrims let it be said, no other
face betrayed hesitation or fear. Whatever was in their
hearts, men, women, and children all took up their bur-
dens and set forth up the hill.

They found the company gathered in a circle on that
spot where, later, the meetinghouse was to be.

"Let us look to God in prayer," said John Carver
simply, and every head was bowed. The service was a
short one, but at the end of it the anxious faces had re-
laxed, the women smiled again, and even Granny
Fletcher dried her eyes. William Bradford, feeling a tug
at his coat, turned about quickly.

"It is not true that there is naught for us to eat,"
Andrew told him in an excited whisper. "I was digging,
just for play, in one of those mounds of earth—look,
there are a dozen of them along the shore. They must
have been the savage men's treasure houses, for see what
I have found within!"

He poured into Bradford's hand a stream of something
red-yellow like gold. It was not mere metal, however,
but something far more precious, the round, ruddy kernels of Indian corn.

The weeks that followed were difficult and full of toil, while there arose slowly upon the hill the little huts built of logs and chinked with mud, and in their midst the square common house that was meetinghouse, arsenal, and granary all in one. Winter drew in, food supplies ran low, and the settlers dipped deeper and deeper into the Indians' corn.

"We will pay the red men for it as soon as we are given opportunity," the elders all agreed; but no one came to claim possession, and no Indians showed their faces where the white men could see.

"I would it were so that we could make payment to somebody," Bradford said more than once to Andrew, yet could offer no solution of the problem of how it was to be done. None of the men approved of taking what was not theirs; but in the face of such famine they knew it was folly to leave the corn untouched.

Andrew did not heed their talk greatly, for he was busier than the rest, being one of the few who had any skill with a fowling piece or a fish line. He was more shabby and ragged than ever, with clumsy patches of leather sewed where his coat had given way, and with a rude cap made of the skin of a fox.

Many nights, however, when he dropped asleep on his bed of straw beside William Bradford's, he would smile to himself in the dark, knowing that he was happier than he had ever been before.

And then came the sickness.

One of the elders, Giles Peabody, was stricken first.

He sat shivering by the fire before the common house at evening, he was burning with fever at midnight, and before sunrise he was dead. Three more were ill on the day that he was buried, and by the next morning there were a dozen. Soon in every family there was someone dead, someone dying; while fewer and fewer were left to go from house to house to care for the sufferers.

William Bradford labored like ten men, and taught Andrew to be nearly as useful as himself. Drusilla Kritchell, although she had her mother and Granny Fletcher sick in her own house, still managed to go forth every day, with all the gravity and earnestness of a grown woman, to nurse and scrub and care for motherless children.

She met Andrew at twilight one evening as both, almost too weary to set one foot before the other, were coming down the hill from the common house.

"My mother is almost well again," she told the boy as he took her basket, "and Granny Fletcher is mending, too, although she is still lightheaded with the fever. But three more of the Peabody children have been taken. I have been with them the whole day."

Andrew followed Drusilla into the house to set down her basket on the table, and there discovered Granny Fletcher huddled in the big chair by the fireplace, for she had refused to stay in bed. She was alternately muttering to herself and babbling aloud.

"So we are to perish after all," she was saying. "A blight lies heavy upon us. Some wrong we must have done. Was it because we took food that was not ours and never repaid? We thought we were starving, but to die in this way is worse than to starve. God has forgotten us. He has hidden his face from us because of our sins."

She turned and saw Andrew standing by the door.

"I said you would bring us ill luck!" she cried. "It was you who broke into the red men's storehouse and laid hands upon what was not ours." Her voice rose high, then dropped suddenly almost to a whisper. "For all the harm and mischief you have done, I forgive you. I will not go before the Judgment Seat thinking ill of any man, not even such as you." She closed her eyes and slipped down limply in the chair, while Drusilla ran to aid her.

"Do not heed what she says!" the girl cried over her shoulder, but the door had closed and Andrew was gone.

Inside the common house on the hill a row of stricken men lay on the straw; but some were mending and none were dying, so that William Bradford had leisure to come forth and sit down by the fire that burned before the door. Silently Andrew came through the dark and found a seat beside him, first flinging a fresh log upon the blaze.

Something stirred outside the circle of ruddy light; then, as the flames leaped from the fresh fuel, there was revealed an ugly yellowish dog that sniffed and skulked among the shadows. Andrew whistled to him, but the creature gave a strange, uncouth yelp of fear and ran away howling.

"That is no dog of ours," the boy observed wonderingly; "where could he have come from?"

"I think he is the same that we caught sight of in those days when we first landed," Bradford answered. "He was with four Indians, the only ones we ever saw."

"It is a strange thing that they never came near us again," Andrew said.

Bradford did not reply at once, so that the two sat in silence for a little. When the older man did speak at last, his voice sounded broken, weary, and listless.

"No, not strange," he remarked slowly. "The Indians fear us and they know how to hide in the forest like foxes. Do you ever think that there may be those whose eyes are always watching us, knowing how we are stricken, counting the dead and waiting—waiting until we are so few that they no longer feel afraid? That dog has waxed very bold. It may be that his masters are waxing bold also."

"We have buried the dead by night and leveled the graves so that no one could count them," declared Andrew huskily, "and we are not quite all gone yet."

"No," said Bradford, "but we are growing perilously few." He was silent again and seemed to go on with difficulty. "I would that we had ever been able to offer payment for that corn we used. I have measured all that we were forced to take and have set a sum of money against it to be ready if the chance for paying should ever come. Perhaps you had better know that it lies in a bag in my chest, so that if—if I should be——"

"Master—Master Bradford," cried Andrew, in agony.

He touched the other's hand and found it burning hot, and saw at last, by a sudden flaring of the fire, that Bradford's face was flushed and his eyes glittering with fever.

"Help me to go inside, boy," he said. "I have been trying to rise these last ten minutes and have not had the strength. It is nothing—nothing, but I think I will go within and lie down beside the others."

Half an hour later Drusilla Kritchell was summoned from the kitchen by an unsteady tap on the outer door. Andrew Newell stood upon the step.

"I must ask a boon of you, since there is no one else to whom I may turn," he said abruptly. "Can you prepare me food to carry on a journey? I am going into the forest to find someone whom I may pay for the grain we have taken."

"Into the forest, alone, to find the Indians?" she exclaimed. "Oh, you must not. It is certain death!"

She looked him up and down in the light of her candle and added bluntly: "You are not even properly clad; your coat is so worn and thin that you will perish with the cold. The sickness will fall upon you all alone in the wilderness."

"It does not matter," he responded indifferently. "Go I must, and if I do not succeed, I will never come back. Will you ask your father, Mistress Drusilla, to tend my master when I am gone? He is stricken with the dire sickness, too. I will come at sunrise to fetch anything you can give me to carry on my way."

He closed the door sharply and vanished into the dark.

The sun was just coming up through the winter fog, a round red ball like a midsummer moon, when Andrew set forth next morning, the little bag of money safe beneath his coat, the scant bundle of Drusilla's provisions under his arm.

A great, long-legged shadow strutted before him, seeming to mock at him and his fantastic errand. To come face to face with the lurking Indians, to explain that the white men had used their corn and wished to repay them, surely it was impossible.

Yet Andrew shook his head doggedly and repeated almost aloud, "If I do not succeed, I will never come back." His devotion to William Bradford and the terrible thought of what the sickness might have wrought before his return dragged at his heart, but he turned his mind resolutely from such thoughts and trudged steadily on.

There was something about his appearance that was not quite as usual. Even the grotesque shadow ahead of him showed it, in that absence of fluttering rags and gaping elbows that had formerly marked his attire. He had a new coat, a warm, substantial one, that bade defiance to all the chill morning winds that could blow.

Granny Fletcher, when she saw him in the doorway receiving his bundle of food from Drusilla, had noticed that something was changed. Her fever had abated a little, nor had it ever been great enough to quench her curiosity.

"See the lad with a whole coat to his back at last!" she exclaimed. "And what a strange color it is—rusty black! Verily, it might be the coat of your black sheep."

Drusilla flushed, said farewell hastily, and closed the door.

"You should not talk; it will bring the shaking fits upon you again," she said sternly as she adjusted the pillow in the big chair.

"You need not have been so quick in closing the door," complained the old woman; "I have no doubt that it was in no proper way that the boy came by that coat. Mercy, child, how heavy-eyed you look this morning! One would think you had not slept. But that coat, I wonder now—"

Drusilla betook herself to another room, not waiting to hear more. The secret of Andrew's new coat was no mystery to her, nor to her younger sister, sleeping profoundly upstairs after a night of intense industry. There was another who shared the secret also, a half-grown sheep, bedded tenderly in the straw of the shed, shivering and indignant at being robbed of its fleece in the dead of winter.

There had long been a story in Drusilla's family that two sisters, one of them her great-grandmother, had, when their father was called away to the wars, sheared one of their sheep, spun and woven the wool, and made him a coat all between sunset and sunrise. Drusilla's spinning wheel and loom had come with her across the sea and stood in the corner of the room where she and her sister slept. There they had both toiled all night, as quickly and skillfully as had that great-grandmother of earlier fame.

"It is a strange color for a coat, but we had no time to dye it," Drusilla apologized, when she gave it to Andrew and bade him put it on. He, in turn, was quite overcome with surprise and gratitude and could hardly form a word of stammering thanks.

A light snow had fallen during the night, showing, as he came into the forest, the lacelike pattern of squirrel and rabbit tracks, and even the deep footprints here and there of larger game. Andrew scanned the ground eagerly for the marks of moccasined feet, yet knew that there was little chance of any Indian leaving a trail so plain. For want of any real direction in which to go, he followed a little stream in whose lower waters he had been used to fish for trout and whose babbling voice seemed to speak to him with cheery friendliness as it led him farther and farther into unknown country.

He ate frugally in the middle of the day, then tramped steadily on until dark. It was growing very cold when he stopped at last, built himself a rough shelter of boughs under an overhanging rock, struck a fire with his flint and steel, and kindled a cheerful blaze. But how small the fire looked in the wide, silent emptiness of the forest!

The rock threw back the heat of the flame, making a warm nook where he curled up and slept comfortably until morning. Once or twice in the night he got up to replenish the fire and to listen to the unfamiliar night sounds of the wood, but each time he was too weary to keep long awake.

When he arose next morning it was colder than ever; his breath went up like smoke in the keen air, and the little brook was frozen solid, its friendly voice silent at last.

This second day's journey into the wilderness seemed to have brought him into a new land. The hills were higher; the great boulders towered above his head; the way was so broken that he had much difficulty in making progress at all. He still clung to the familiar stream as a guide, although it had shrunk now to a tiny thread, just a gleam of ice here and there under the slippery stones and snow-wreathed underbrush.

Night found him weary and spent and utterly disheartened. In all this long journey he had not yet seen a sign of any human being.

With the greatest difficulty, he cut enough boughs for a rude tent, and got together a supply of firewood sufficient for the night. The fuel was wet, his fingers were stiff with cold, so that it was a long time before he could strike a spark and persuade the uncertain flame to creep along the leaves and set fire to the wood.

Since he had not delayed his journey to hunt or fish by the way, his food was almost gone. His strength was almost gone also, as he realized when he got up from beside the fire and crawled into his shelter. He would not be able to journey much farther, yet it was his steady purpose still to go forward. Almost in the act of nestling down among the pine branches, he fell asleep.

A troubled dream aroused him many hours later. Vaguely he was conscious that he must get up and mend the fire or it would die out and leave him to freeze. It took him some minutes to summon enough resolution, but at last, with a great effort, he stirred, crawled out of his refuge, came forth into the light, and then shrank back again with a gasp of overwhelming astonishment.

For there, standing beside the glowing coals motionless as a statue, silent as the still forest itself, was a gigantic Indian.

For a moment there was no move made, no word spoken, as Andrew crouched staring at the stranger, at the hawklike face, at the firelight shining on the dull red of his naked arms and knees, at his misshapen shadow that danced on the snow behind him.

Then at last the other, without moving his head or changing his expression, spoke quietly.

"You welcome—here," he said in slow, broken English.

Later, Andrew was to learn that many of the red men had learned English from the British sailors who manned the fishing boats coasting along the New England shore, and that this man had even made a voyage with one of them.

At that moment, however, it seemed to the boy nothing other than a miracle that here, in this far, silent wilderness, he should hear his own tongue spoken.

The Indian drew out, from somewhere in the folds of his scanty garments, a slice of dried meat and set it to broil before the fire. Andrew sniffed wistfully at the delicious odor of its cooking, but when the red man silently offered it to him, he shook his head, so firm was his determination that no Indian should know how near the white men were to starvation.

The man merely nodded quietly at his refusal,

brought out more meat and some dried fish, and put the whole before the fire. He looked so long and steadily at the boy that Andrew felt no detail of thin cheeks and hollow eyes were escaping that keen stare. Then the piercing glance moved onward to where the remains of Drusilla's provisions lay upon the ground, a few broken crusts of bread and a bit of cheese.

The stranger made no comment, but very carefully completed his cooking, spread the feast upon a piece of bark, and pushed it toward Andrew. With one lean red hand he made a gesture in the direction of the settlement.

"All hungry—starving; we know. Dying—we know that, too," he said.

"You—you have seen," faltered Andrew, thrown out of his reserve by this sudden statement.

"You bury dead by night." The man nodded slowly. "You smooth graves, we count graves—morning." He thrust the food forward again and said peremptorily, "Eat."

And eat Andrew did, since there was no use for further pretense. There was a little talk between them as his strange visitor plied him with food; but it was not until the ravenous meal was ended and the boy had pushed away his bark plate that he made any attempt to speak of the errand for which he had come such a long and weary way.

"There was some corn left buried near the shore where we landed," he began. "We used it and we wish to make payment. See, I have here the proper sum of money."

He brought out from under his coat William Bradford's bag of coins.

But the Indian shook his head.

"The corn not mine," he said.

"Then to whom did it belong? Where are the men who left it there?"

"All dead," the other answered. "The great sickness —it took them all away. Only one left. He live with our tribe."

"Then take the money to him," begged Andrew. "We counted carefully and wish to pay for every measure. Look, it is all here. Will you take him what should be his?"

He poured the contents of the bag into the Indian's unresponsive hand, a heap of silver and copper coins, with a few of gold. The man turned them over with little interest, letting some of them drop and disappear in the snow and the ashes. His eyes brightened, however, when he saw among them a big copper penny piece that was new enough to shine a little still and to wink in the firelight with a pleasant glow. Andrew, seeing what attracted him, gathered up such of the fallen coins as he could find and polished them on the rough sleeve of his coat.

Then he fetched a handful of sand from the tiny bank that he had noticed beside the stream and scoured the money until the silver gleamed and the copper glowed and burned in the red light of the flame. The gold did not reflect the fire and was only dulled by the scraping with sand so that, in the end, the Indian cast it aside as he received the rest of the money eagerly.

"He shall have it all, that Tisquantum—he is last of tribe, and maybe someday I bring him to you and he show you how to plant the corn for nex' year. You would not harm him."

"I will swear it," Andrew answered. "Does he really fear the white men?"

"All of us fear you. Surely you mus' know it."

"We have some brave men among us," Andrew said, "and a soldier who is a famous fighter to be our leader."

"Ugh, you mean round small man in red coat who go tramping through forest, musket on shoulder, breaking through the bushes and making much noise as giant moose. We could slay him many times with arrows; he mus' have known it, yet he not afraid. No, it is not this man, nor all your fighting men we fear."

"What is it, then?" Andrew asked, much puzzled.

Half by signs, half in his imperfect English, the Indian sought to explain. And so vivid were his gestures, so potent his few words, that finally Andrew began to understand.

It was the strange spirit of the English that the Indians did not comprehend. When the red men were hungry, when sickness came upon them, even when they were weary of the spot where they dwelt, they gathered up their goods and moved to some new camping place. When the plague first fell upon the tribe that dwelt where the white man did now, they broke and scattered, carrying the same death to all who were near. Their people died in numbers past any counting; yet even now they were many more than the newcomers.

But with the white man it was not the same. The men had died, and the women, but they did not run away. They went on with their daily tasks, although they were fewer and fewer. The Indians thought that the courage of those who were gone must pass into the hearts of those who still lived, and even though so many should perish that there was but one left, they would still fear him, since he would have the strength of all.

Very slowly Andrew turned this strange idea over and over in his mind.

"And we wonder at you, in our turn," the boy replied at last, "how you can find food and live in plenty in what seems to us a cruel and barren wilderness. If we could learn to be friends, white men and red men, how we could help each other in many things!"

So they made their compact of peace and friendliness there by the fire in the heart of the frozen wilderness, with the blue wood smoke drifting above their heads and floating away over the treetops.

Afterward, when the Indian said that they should sleep for a little to prepare for their next day's journey, they lay down side by side in the warm glow of the blaze; and since Andrew had traveled far, had eaten fully, and was quite worn out, he fell quickly asleep.

He awoke, much later, with a start, to find himself alone, with the newly replenished fire crackling beside him, with a package of deer meat and corn laid close to his hand, and with the dawn breaking behind the dark pines.

He made his way homeward more easily than he had come, for he knew the country now and could follow the stream without so much picking and choosing of the way.

Although he was free from one anxiety, there was still a heavy burden upon his heart, for he could not put from him the remembrance of William Bradford—the man who had his whole-souled devotion—of how he had sat shivering by the fire with the shadow of the dreadful sickness already upon him.

He hurried faster and faster, feeling that the dense wood hemmed him in and held him back— that he would never reach his journey's end and hear tidings of his master.

He was free of the forest at last and hastening across the stump-dotted slope to the huddle of cabins beside the stream. How few they looked! He had almost forgotten what a tiny handful of dwellings the settlement was.

He was panting as he ran down the worn path, dashed through the empty street, and thundered at the door of the common house. It was growing dark; there was no light within nor any voice to answer his impatient knock.

Trembling, hesitating in dread of what he might find, he opened the door and stepped over the threshold. Five men had lain on the straw the night of his departure; there was only one now. At the sound of his footstep, this one stirred as though roused from sleep, turned his head, and spoke. It was William Bradford.

"Four days you were gone," Bradford said at last, after he had heard the hurried substance of Andrew's adventures. "Much can happen in such a place as this in four days. Enoch Fullerton and old Phineas Hall have gone from us, but the others who were suffering here have got well and gone about their business.

"And as for me, four days were enough for the coming of the fever and its burning out, so that I shall soon be a whole man again. Now tell me that strange tale all over again; I must have not heard aright, for surely what you say is past belief."

Andrew went over his story, repeating every word of his talk in the forest with the Indian.

"They know more about us than we dreamed possible," he said, "but we need no longer fear them. And they think, poor blind savages, that, as we grow fewer, the spirit of those who have passed still dwells in those who remain."

There was a little pause, for Bradford, like Andrew, must consider this idea carefully.

"Not so blind," he said finally; "savages and heathen, yet not so blind. Do you never think that the spirit of this adventure lies not in the elders, the older men like me, but in the young men, the youths and children—in you?

"We shall soon be gone, for age passes quickly; it is

youth that must take up our purpose; it is on youth that the weight of it all depends. Even this errand of yours, without youth it would never have been accomplished; we should have gone on wasting our days in doubt and dread, fearing to turn our hands to the real conquering of the wilderness."

The door opened in the twilight and several men came in, John Carver and three of the elders. Bradford raised his voice that they might hear.

"This lad has succeeded in that madcap expedition from which we have all been saying that he would never come back. He has made good our debt to the Indians and has brought back good tidings and such an understanding of the red men as we could never have gained for ourselves. After this service he shall no longer be my bound servant, but a citizen of this community. Andrew Newell, whom we were calling a foolhardy boy, has shown himself to be a man."

Thereafter it was necessary for Andrew to sit down upon the straw again and tell the whole story once more, that John Carver and the elders might marvel anew at his tale.

It was not until an hour later that he was suffered at last to pass out of the building and go down the little street to carry his news and his thanks to Drusilla Kritchell. The air was soft after the long days of cold; there was promise in it that this harsh country's climate held spring as well as winter.

Granny Fletcher, who was well enough now to limp

out to the doorstep, was sitting on the wide stone, wrapped in Drusilla's cloak, while Peter Perkins, coming up the path, had just stopped to speak to her.

Tidings of what Andrew had done seemed to have run before him, for Peter Perkins took off his broad hat and greeted him with a "Good even to you, sir."

"What is that?" Andrew heard in a shrill whisper from the old woman, who had evidently not yet learned the news. "Do you call that wicked lad 'sir,' and take off your hat to him?"

"We may have been mistaken in him, after all," Peter Perkins returned in a whisper just as audible; "and it is as well to show respect to one who is now a citizen of our colony and who wears a good coat upon his back. It is little one can tell of what the future holds!"

Becky's Thanksgiving Turkey

Constance L. Skinner

🍁🍁

Becky Landers, being the man of the family, knew that if there was to be turkey on the Thanksgiving dinner table, she would have to provide it. And the younger members of the household had decreed turkey. With Ted, aged seven, and Ruth, aged five and a half, the point was already settled.

Their mother only said, "It would be nice to give them what they want at Thanksgiving time. There's so little we give the children in Kentucky—except peril." Her blue eyes misted with sorrow.

Becky's throat contracted sharply. She could not accustom herself to the change that had come over her once-playful, merry mother since that terrible day when raiding Indians from Kaskaskia had captured Rodney. Mrs. Landers was a devoted and a companionable mother to all her children, but her eldest, Rodney, had been a little closer to her than the others; perhaps because her husband's death had made her so much more dependent upon her son.

On the frontier a boy of sixteen was a man, a soldier, a provider, and a strong arm of protection for the women and children not of his household alone, but of his settlement. And in these first years of the Revolution, when, on the Atlantic seaboard, two opposing ideals of government grappled like giants towering and swaying against the flushing dawn sky of Freedom, a blood-red shadow was cast over Kentucky.

That fierce warrior and prophet, Dragging Canoe, had warned the first white man who had purchased land in the red man's "Beloved Old Fields"—which is the meaning of the name Kentucky—that they would find it "a dark and bloody ground." Ever since the planting of the first settlement, the Indians from all sides had been doing their best to fulfill Dragging Canoe's prophecy.

Whole settlements had been wiped out, and men, women, and children slain or carried away to whatever fate the whim of their captors might dictate—some to be murdered on the march in a moment of angry caprice, others to be burned in the Indian towns in celebration of the victory, and a few to be saved and adopted into the tribe.

"Mother," Becky said gently, "we well know how the Indians love strength and courage and a handsome look. Those who came here as friends always admired Rod so much because he was so tall and straight, and could run and jump and shoot and wrestle as well as any of their own boys. They didn't kill Rod, Mother. I *know* they didn't. I just *know* it."

She kissed her mother, then went swiftly across the kitchen, took down her rifle, slung her powder horn around her neck and her shot pouch at her waist; and, after adjusting her beaver cap somewhat rakishly over her mass of brown curls, she turned in the doorway and said:

"Now for the Thanksgiving turkey!"

"Becky," her mother called after her anxiously, "don't go out of sight."

Becky waved her hand and tramped swiftly on. Mother always said that; poor, grieved, terrified Mother. But, as Becky knew, deer and turkey and buffalo did not come nosing up against the walls of the fort offering to replenish the harassed white men's larder. As her friend, the old scout Simon Kenton often said:

"Food's for life; an' if you want food in Kaintuck today, you've got to risk your life to git it."

It did not seem at all strange to Becky Landers that she should be setting off on this crisp, white, sunny twenty-fourth of November with a man's rifle over her shoulder on the dangerous quest for turkey, instead of stitching lace flounces on a party dress as most other girls of fifteen might be doing at that time.

Becky had never had a "party dress," possibly she had never seen a lace flounce; and the preparation of any jolly entertainment in the protection and security of a civilized home was an experience she had never known.

Becky's dress in winter was a long-fringed deerskin jerkin over deerskin or fur short trousers and leggings. Her boots were moccasins. In the summer she wore a one-piece linsey-woolsey frock of her own or her mother's spinning.

She danced almost as much perhaps as any belle in the proud social heights of Charleston or Philadelphia; but in every gay turn of the old English country dance she knew precisely where her rifle hung on the log wall. She could reach it in a few lithe wildcat leaps if the door flung open to let some breathless messenger shout:

"Injuns! Get into the fort!"

Or if, across the fiddler's merry tune, cut the low, chilling "Hooh-yeh-hoo-hoo" of the war whoop.

In a city or a safe country village, Becky Landers would have been called a tomboy, because she had always been fonder of boys' sports than of girlish amusements. On the frontier, her swift running and jumping, her good marksmanship, and her native intelligence on the trail—what we might call her good scout work—and her utter fearlessness had given her enviable fame. From Boonesborough and Harrodsburg to Crab Orchard the settlers knew the name of Becky Landers and respected it. To Becky herself, she seemed in no way remarkable.

She was without vanity and she had a very practical mind. When Indians had killed her father, as the caravan of which the Landers family was a part came through Cumberland Gap into Kentucky, her brother Rodney, two years older than herself, had become the head of the family, its provider and protector. When, later, other savages from Kaskaskia had captured Rodney and taken him away, it had devolved on Becky to become the man of the family. She was that man to the best of her ability.

So far from admiring herself, Becky was reckoning her limitations as she set out after her Thanksgiving turkey. She could hunt, yes; but she could not fight. When the frontiersmen of Maybrook took the warpath themselves to assist some other settlement in driving off the Indian bands which the British Governor Hamilton, of Detroit, sent down on Kentucky from time to time, she was never mustered among the warriors. They called her a "girl" then. The warpath was "no place for girls!"

How could she ever hope to find Rod if they would not let her go with George Rogers Clark and his men when they made their planned raid on Kaskaskia? Becky had heard of the plans of that notable young Kentucky soldier. Clark said that the settlements in Kentucky could not stand if they remained solely on the defensive. He was for the bold stroke!

"If Virginia will only send me the powder and lead I've asked for," he had told Simon Kenton, "I'll take two hundred and fifty men and rush down on Kaskaskia and Vincennes and capture them before the enemy know we're there! They are the keys of the Illinois country. With them I'll go on and lock out the British at Detroit. Some say it's not Governor Hamilton but that queer, sallow-faced devil, Major Hay, who is responsible for this Indian business. But, whoever it is, he'll loose no more savages down on Kentucky. If Virginia'll only send me the powder!"

Even several of the bravest men in Kentucky thought Clark's scheme a folly and Clark himself a madman. Becky didn't. They said, "He's brave, but he's too young to have much sense about a big thing like that."

Becky disagreed with them. To her, aged fifteen, Clark, who was twenty-three, was not "young." She wished that she knew him, and that he lived in Maybrook, her own settlement, instead of Louisville, which was so far away.

"I believe I could make him let me go on the dash to Kaskaskia," she mused. "He'd understand."

Her mind ran on, recalling all the various things she had heard men say of Clark. For instance, they said how different he was from Daniel Boone, the other outstanding figure in Kentucky. Boone was much older, of course; and he was mild and affable, a man to be loved and trusted at sight, a wise man, too, intelligent, experienced.

But Clark! Clark was the wildest "white Indian" the frontier had ever seen. He was fierce, violent, rash beyond all sanity! A man to be feared. Yet, they were forced to admit it, Clark was loved, too, and trusted. He was honest. His word was good. And he had an uncanny power over other men. The worst ruffians and bandits in Kentucky fell into line at his nod. They adored him.

Then, too, the women had only good words for him. He was so handsome, with his well set-up body, his brownish-blond hair, his finely cut mouth and power-fully shaped head, and his eyes that flashed a whitish gray in anger, or, in his pleasant moods, were as vividly and tenderly blue as the spring sky. He was kind and chivalrous always to women of all ages; and every woman in Kentucky sang his praises.

"I just *know* Clark would take me to Kaskaskia to look for Rod," said Becky to herself again.

Through the leafless boughs of the winter-stripped trees she could see the river. A stretch of unbroken white lay between the forest fringe where she stood and the bank of the broad stream. It had been an unusually mild winter thus far. The ground was only lightly thatched with snow; and the river was open. The sun dropped a mellow warm light from a cloudless sky.

Becky had walked rapidly for two hours and had long ago left the fort far behind. She knew that there was comparatively little danger of a raid in winter. Summer was the Indians' war season. And sometimes, in the brief warm spell toward the end of autumn, the red men came down again for one last attack before winter should seal up the land. That is why the frontiersmen called that brief warm spell "Indian summer."

While it was not likely that a war party was lurking about, Becky had kept a careful lookout for Indian signs. So far she had not seen a human track, except those which marked the trail behind her. Nor had she seen a turkey.

Now, suddenly, both human beings and turkeys appeared at once. On the river, swinging down midstream, she espied a large boat. It was apparently heading for the shore directly in front of her, and it was a white man's boat.

She was about to run across the fifty yards or so of open space to the landing place when she caught sight of turkey feathers. There was her Thanksgiving dinner, pecking through the snow among the thick bushes on the bank's rim. She counted them by tails—one turkey, two, three, another, more still, a flock of a dozen, perhaps eighteen! And in a few minutes the boatmen would ground on the shore, startle the whole flock and send them swiftly winging over the river, perhaps, and high into blue heavens of unattainable desire!

It was a terrible situation for the young hunter. The low bushes were so thick that she could not see the birds at all, only those tantalizing tails. Her only chance of bagging a turkey was to fire at once at the spot where, judging from its tail feathers, the nearest turkey should be.

Becky dropped down behind a log, propped her heavy, long-barreled rifle on it, steadying it with the thick moss pad she carried for that purpose, took careful aim, and fired. The result of her shot was such that her heart almost leaped out of her mouth.

With a wild yell a dozen redskins jumped up from among the bushes, their turkey-feather headdresses tossing in the air. Almost instantly one Indian fell, his heart pierced by a shot from the boat. More shots cracked from the boat, and took deadly effect. Becky's mind worked as fast as her fingers, which were rapidly reloading her rifle, this time with more than bird shot.

She grasped the full seriousness of her predicament. She had stumbled upon an ambush. Whoever the white men in the big boat were, the Indians had received word of their coming and had been lying in wait to kill them. But for the fact that Becky Landers was looking for a Thanksgiving turkey, and had fired at a bunch of tail feathers, the white men would have been shot down as they landed.

She could guess what was taking place in the minds of the savages. They believed that they, in their turn, had been ambushed. The shot from behind meant to them not that Becky Landers was trying for a turkey, but that armed white men were screened in the woods. Becky knew that her only hope of escape was to intensify that impression.

She must keep on firing as fast as she could reload, to discourage the Indians from rushing into her bit of forest. She knew that, when Indians discovered they were in a trap, they seldom stayed to fight; they usually broke through and made off.

Bang! Her second shot rhymed with a volley from the boat. The savages caught up their wounded and dashed westward along the bank. Far down the river a large canoe slid out from the opposite shore to meet them. Becky lay still, peering over the log's edge, and watched their flight. As she lay concealed she heard a voice calling:

"Hullo-oo, there!" A white man, followed by seven others, came up over the edge of the bank. He called again, "Hullo, there! Come on out, you fellows, and let's shake hands with you."

"Hullo!" Becky's clear light tones floated back to him and gave him such a shock that he almost dropped his rifle; and the sight of Becky running toward him fleetly across the snowy flat did nothing to reassure him.

"A girl!" he shouted. "A girl, by thunder!"

"Three cheers for the girl!" another man cried. The men, including their leader, gave the cheers lustily. They laughed in mischievous delight as they saw her cheeks grow crimson.

"Why, it's Becky Landers!"

Becky looked quickly at the speaker. Gradually, through the haze of her embarrassment, she recognized him, and then the man next to him. They were Bill Canty and Jeff Smoke, two ruffians who had been driven out of Maybrook more than a year before. A sense of real fear, which the Indians had not inspired, came over her. Who were these eight men and why had they come?

She looked again anxiously at their leader and took some comfort from his handsome, manly face and the blue eyes which beamed on her with frank admiration and kindness. Still, she had to know; and, according to her habit, she went straight to the point.

"Are you a highwayman, too?" she asked, looking him bravely in the eyes.

"Sort of," he answered, his white teeth showing in a flashing smile.

"Because if you are," she went on steadily, though she felt her knees beginning to shake, "I haven't anything but my rifle. And we need that so terribly. You see, I have to take care of Mother and the children."

"That's right," Jeff Smoke put in. "She's the man o' the family ever since the Injuns run off with her brother."

The leader put out his hand and grasped hers.

"Becky Landers," he said, "you're a first-class fighting man and we're proud to know you. Maybe you've heard of me. My name's Clark."

"Not George Rogers Clark!" she gasped, her eyes getting rounder and larger.

"That's me, Becky." He laughed.

"But you said you were a highwayman!"

"Well, that's the mildest name they're calling me back in Virginia right now," he answered. "You see, I've got a boatload of powder down below. The Virginia Assembly wouldn't vote it to me because they said they couldn't afford it. So I told them, if they didn't, I'd raise three or four hundred men out here and take Kentucky for myself—"

"We could do it, too, b'gosh!" Bill Canty exclaimed.

" 'For,' said I, 'gentlemen, if you think Kentucky is not worth defending you can't think it worth holding, so it'll be no loss to you.' They were afraid I meant it. So they gave me the powder. But the governor said I was no better than 'a highwayman.' Now you see why I answered 'sort of' when you asked me."

"I see," Becky answered, dimpling.

"And, Becky Landers, if the Indians had killed me and my friends here, and had captured the powder, it's likely the British would have taken Kentucky. That powder's going along in our powder horns, Becky, to Kaskaskia and Vincennes. When you shot at those savages, Becky Landers, maybe you fired the shot that'll save Kentucky."

"I didn't fire at savages," Becky said. She was far too truthful to accept praise she felt was not deserved. "I only saw their tails—I mean—I thought they were turkeys. And I had promised the babies a Thanksgiving turkey."

She colored hotly again as a roar of mirth went around.

"Jeff," said Clark, as soon as he could speak, "run down to the boat and fetch the two turkeys I shot this morning."

"Right enough," Jeff agreed, and jumped over the bank. When he returned, Clark took the turkeys and slung them over his shoulder.

"You boys can eat deer," he said. "And you'd better fall to as soon as you've pitched camp. I'll sleep at Kenton's tonight. But first I'm going home with Becky Landers and her Thanksgiving turkeys. I want to tell Mrs. Landers what a great soldier her daughter is.

"You needn't blush, Becky Landers. Even if you did shoot just because you thought they were turkeys, you kept on after you knew they were Indians. It took brains to know that was the best thing to do, and it took courage to do it. When we eat dinner in Kaskaskia, boys, we'll drink the first toast to Becky Landers, the lass who saved our powder."

"You bet we will!" they shouted.

Becky's heart was thumping as she turned back through the snowy woods, where the blue shadows of dusk were beginning to fall, with George Rogers Clark at her side. The trail they traveled was the one she had made earlier in the day on her hunt for the Thanksgiving turkey, and now it led them back to the Landers' cabin under the walls of the Maybrook fort.

But to Becky Landers every softly crunching print of her small moccasined foot beside his on that homeward trail seemed to mark another step forward on the road to Kaskaskia and Rodney.

If I Were a Pilgrim Child
Rowena Bennett

If I were a Pilgrim child,
   Dressed in white or gray,
I should catch my turkey wild
   For Thanksgiving Day.
I should pick my cranberries
   Fresh from out a bog,
And make a table of a stump
   And sit upon a log.
An Indian would be my guest
   And wear a crimson feather,
And we should clasp our hands and say
   Thanksgiving grace together.

But I was born in modern times
   And shall not have this joy.

My cranberries will be delivered
  By the grocery boy.
My turkey will be served upon
  A shining silver platter.
It will not taste as wild game tastes
  Though it will be much fatter;
And, oh, of all the guests that come
  Not one of them will wear
Moccasins upon his feet
  Or feathers in his hair!

The Kingdom of the Greedy
P. J. Stahl

The Country of the Greedy, well known in history, was ruled by a king who had much trouble. His subjects were well behaved, but they had one sad fault: they were too fond of pies and tarts.

It was as disagreeable to them to swallow a spoonful of soup as if it were so much sea water, and it would take a policeman to make them open their mouths for a bit of meat, either boiled or roasted.

This deplorable taste not only made the fortunes of the pastry cooks, but also of the apothecaries. Families ruined themselves in pills and powders; camomile, rhubarb, and peppermint trebled in price, as well as other disagreeable remedies, such as castor—which I will not name.

The King of the Greedy sought long for the means

of correcting this fatal passion for sweets, but even the faculty were puzzled.

"Your Majesty," said the great court doctor Olibriers at his last audience, "your people look like putty! They are incurable; their senseless love for good eating will bring them all to the grave."

This view of things did not suit the King. He was wise, and saw very plainly that a monarch without subjects would be but a sorry king.

Happily, after this utter failure of the doctors, there came into the mind of His Majesty a first-class idea: he telegraphed for Mother Mitchel, the most celebrated of all pastry cooks. Mother Mitchel soon arrived, with her black cat, Fanfreluche, who accompanied her everywhere. He was an incomparable cat. He had not his equal as an adviser and a taster of tarts.

Mother Mitchel, having respectfully inquired what she and her cat could do for His Majesty, the King demanded of the astonished pastry cook a tart as big as the Capitol—bigger even, if possible, but no smaller.

When the King uttered this astounding order, deep emotion was shown by the chamberlains, the pages, and lackeys. Nothing but the respect due to his presence prevented them from crying "Long live Your Majesty!" in his very ears. But the King had seen enough of the enthusiasm of the populace, and did not allow such sounds in the recesses of his palace.

The King gave Mother Mitchel one month to carry out his gigantic project. "It is enough," she proudly

replied, brandishing her crutch. Then, taking leave of
the King, she and her cat set out for their home.

On the way Mother Mitchel arranged in her head the
plan of the monument which was to immortalize her,
and considered the means of executing it. As to its form
and size, it was to be as exact a copy of the Capitol as
possible, since the King had willed it; but its outside
crust should have a beauty all its own. The dome must
be adorned with sugar plums of all colors and sur-
mounted by a splendid crown of macaroons, spun sugar,
chocolate, and candied fruits. It was no small affair.

Mother Mitchel did not like to lose her time. Her
plan of battle once formed, she recruited on her way
all the little pastry cooks of the country, as well as all
the tiny six-year-olds who had a sincere love for the noble
callings of scullion and apprentice. There were plenty
of these, as you may suppose, in the Country of the
Greedy; Mother Mitchel had her pick of them.

Mother Mitchel, with the help of her crutch and of
Fanfreluche, who miaowed loud enough to be heard
twenty miles off, called upon all the millers of the land
and commanded them to bring together at a certain
time as many sacks of fine flour as they could grind in a
week.

There were only windmills in that country; you may
easily believe how they all began to go. B-r-r-r-r! What
a noise they made! The clatter was so great that all the
birds flew away to other climes, and even the clouds fled
from the sky.

At the call of Mother Mitchel all the farmers' wives

were set to work; they rushed to the hen coops to collect the seven thousand fresh eggs that Mother Mitchel wanted for her great edifice. Deep was the emotion of the fowls. The hens were inconsolable, and the unhappy creatures mourned upon the palings for the loss of all their hopes.

The milkmaids were busy from morning till night in milking cows. Mother Mitchel must have twenty thousand pails of milk. All the little calves were put on half rations. This great work was nothing to them, and they complained pitifully to their mothers. Many of the cows protested with energy against this unreasonable tax, which made their young families so uncomfortable. There were pails upset, and even some milkmaids went head over heels. But these little accidents did not chill the enthusiasm of the laborers.

And now Mother Mitchel called for a thousand pounds of the best butter. All the churns for twenty miles around began to work in the most lively manner. Their dashers dashed without ceasing, keeping perfect time. The butter was tasted, rolled into pats, wrapped up, and put into baskets. Such energy had never been known before.

Mother Mitchel passed for a sorceress. It was all because of her cat, Fanfreluche, with whom she had mysterious doings and pantomimes, and with whom she talked in her inspired moments as if he were a real person.

Certainly, since the famous "Puss in Boots" there had never been an animal so extraordinary; and credulous folks suspected him of being a magician. Some curious people had the courage to ask Fanfreluche if this were true; but he replied by bristling and showing his teeth and claws so fiercely that the conversation had ended there. Sorceress or not, Mother Mitchel was always obeyed. No one else was ever served so punctually.

On the appointed day all the millers arrived with their asses trotting in single file, each laden with a great sack of flour. Mother Mitchel, after having examined the quality of the flour, had every sack accurately weighed. This was head work and hard work, and took time; but Mother Mitchel was untiring, and her cat, also, for while the operation lasted he sat on the roof watching.

It is only just to say that the millers of the Greedy Kingdom brought flour not only faultless but of full weight. They knew that Mother Mitchel was not joking when she said that others must be as exact with her as she was with them. Perhaps also they were a little afraid of the cat, whose great green eyes were always shining upon them like two round lamps, and never lost sight of them for one moment.

All the farmers' wives arrived in turn, with baskets of eggs upon their heads. They did not load their donkeys with them, for fear that in joggling along they would become omelettes on the way. Mother Mitchel received them with her usual gravity. She had the patience to look through every egg to see if it were fresh.

She did not wish to run the risk of having young

chickens in a tart that was destined for those who could not bear the taste of any meat however tender and delicate. The number of eggs was complete, and again Mother Mitchel and her cat had nothing to complain of.

This Greedy nation, though carried away by love of good eating, was strictly honest. It must be said that where nations are patriotic, desire for the common good makes them unselfish. Mother Mitchel's tart was to be the glory of the country and each one was proud to contribute to such a great work.

And now the milkmaids with their pots and pails of milk, and the butter makers with their baskets filled with the rich yellow pats of butter, filed in long procession to the right and left of the cabin of Mother Mitchel.

There was no need for her to examine so carefully the butter and the milk. She had such a delicate nose that if there had been a single pat of ancient butter or a pail of sour milk she would have pounced upon it instantly. But all was perfectly fresh.

In that golden age they did not understand the art, now so well known, of making milk out of flour and water. Real milk was necessary to make cheese cakes and ice cream and other delicious confections much adored in the Greedy Kingdom. If anyone had made such a despicable discovery, he would have been chased from the country as a public nuisance.

Then came the grocers, with their aprons of coffee bags, and with the jolly, mischievous faces the rogues always have. Each one clasped to his heart a sugar loaf nearly as large as himself, whose summit, without its paper cap, looked like new-fallen snow upon a pyramid. Mother Mitchel, with her crutch for a baton, saw them all placed in her storerooms upon shelves put up for the purpose.

She had to be very strict, for some of the little fellows could hardly part from their merchandise, and many were indiscreet, with their tongues behind their mountains of sugar. If they had been let alone, they would never have stopped till the sugar was all gone. But they had not thought of the implacable eye of old Fanfreluche, who, posted upon a water spout, took note of all their misdeeds.

From another quarter came a whole army of country people, rolling wheelbarrows and carrying huge baskets, all filled with cherries, plums, peaches, apples, and pears.

All these fruits were so fresh, in such perfect condition, with their fair shining skins, that they looked like wax or painted marble, but their delicious perfume proved that they were real. Some little people hidden in the corners took pains to find this out. Between ourselves, Mother Mitchel made believe not to see them, and took the precaution of holding Fanfreluche in her arms so that he could not spring upon them.

The fruits were all put into bins, each kind by itself. And now the preparations were finished. There was no time to lose before setting to work.

The spot which Mother Mitchel had chosen for her great edifice was a pretty hill on which a plateau formed a splendid site. This hill commanded the capitol city, built upon the slope of another hill close by.

After having beaten down the earth till it was smooth as a floor, they spread over it loads of bread crumbs, brought from the bakers', and leveled it with rake and spade, as we do gravel in our garden walks.

Little birds, as greedy as themselves, came in flocks to the feast, but they might eat as they liked, it would never be missed, so thick was the carpet. It was a great chance for the bold little things.

All the ingredients for the tart were now ready. Upon order of Mother Mitchel they began to peel the apples and pears and to take out the pits. The weather was so pleasant that the girls sat out-of-doors, upon the ground, in long rows. The sun looked down upon them with a merry face.

Each of the little workers had a big earthen pan, and peeled incessantly the apples which the boys brought them. When the pans were full, they were carried away and others were brought. They had also to carry away the peels, or the girls would have been buried in them. Never was there such a peeling before.

Not far away the children were stoning the plums, cherries, and peaches. This work, being the easiest, was given to the youngest and most inexperienced hands, which were all first carefully washed, for Mother Mitchel, though not very particular about her own toilet, was very neat in her cooking.

The schoolhouse, long unused (for in the Country of

the Greedy they had forgotten everything), was arranged for the second class of workers, and the cat was their inspector. He walked around and around, growling if he saw the fruit popping into any of the little mouths. If they had dared, how they would have pelted him with plum stones! But no one risked it. Fanfreluche was not to be trifled with.

In those days powdered sugar had not been invented, and to grate it all was no small affair. It was the work that the grocers used to dislike most; both lungs and arms were soon tired. But Mother Mitchel was there to sustain them with her unequaled energy. She chose the laborers from the most robust of the boys. With mallet and knife she broke the cones into round pieces, and they grated them till they were too small to hold.

The bits were put into baskets to be pounded. One would never have expected to find all the thousand pounds of sugar again. But a new miracle was wrought by Mother Mitchel. It was all there!

It was then the turn of the ambitious scullions to enter the lists and break the seven thousand eggs for Mother Mitchel. It was not hard to break them—any fool could do that; but to separate adroitly the yolks and the whites demands some talent, and, above all, great care. We dare not say that there were no accidents here, no eggs too well scrambled, no baskets upset.

But the experience of Mother Mitchel had counted upon such things, and it may truly be said that there were never so many eggs broken at once, or ever could be again. To make an omelette of them would have taken a saucepan as large as a skating pond, and the fattest cook that ever lived could not hold the handle of such a saucepan.

But this was not all. Now that the yolks and whites were once divided, they must each be beaten separately in wooden bowls, to give them the necessary lightness. The egg beaters were marshaled into two big brigades, the yellow and the white. Everyone preferred the white for it was much more amusing to make those snowy masses that rose up so high than to beat the yolks, which knew no better than to mix together like so much sauce.

Mother Mitchel, with her usual wisdom, had avoided this difficulty by casting lots. Thus, those who were not on the white side had no reason to complain of oppression. And truly, when all was done, the whites and the yellows were equally tired. All had cramps in their hands.

Now began the real labor of Mother Mitchel. Till now she had been the commander-in-chief—the head only; now she put her own finger in the pie. First, she had to make the sweetmeats and jam out of all the immense quantity of fruit she had stored. For this, as she could only do one kind at a time, she had ten kettles, each as big as a dinner table.

During forty-eight hours the cooking went on; a dozen scullions blew the fire and put on the fuel. Mother Mitchel, with a spoon that four modern cooks could hardly lift, never ceased stirring and trying the boiling fruit. Three expert tasters, chosen from the most dainty, had orders to report progress every half-hour.

It is unnecessary to state that all the sweetmeats were

perfectly successful, or that they were of exquisite consistency, color, and perfume. With Mother Mitchel there was no such word as *fail*. When each kind of sweetmeat was finished, she skimmed it, and put it away to cool in enormous bowls before potting.

She did not use for this the usual little glass or earthen jars, but great stone ones, like those in the *Forty Thieves*. Not only did these take less time to fill, but they were safe from the children. The scum and the scrapings were something, to be sure. But there was little Toto, who thought this was not enough. He would have jumped into one of the bowls if they had not held him.

Mother Mitchel, who thought of everything, had ordered two hundred great kneading troughs, wishing that all the utensils of this great work should be perfectly new. These two hundred troughs, like her other materials, were all delivered punctually and in good order.

The pastry cooks rolled up their sleeves and began to knead the dough with cries of "Hi! Hi!" that could be heard for miles.

It was odd to see this army of bakers in serried ranks, all making the same gestures at once, like well-disciplined soldiers, stooping and rising together in time, so that a foreign ambassador wrote to his court that he wished his people could load and fire as well as these would knead. Such praise a people never forgets.

When each troughful of paste was approved it was moulded with care into the form of bricks, and with the aid of the engineer-in-chief, a young genius who had gained the first prize in the school of architecture, the majestic edifice was begun.

Mother Mitchel herself drew the plan; in following her directions, the young engineer showed himself modest beyond all praise. He had the good sense to understand that the architecture of tarts and pies had rules of its own, and that therefore the experience of Mother Mitchel was worth all the scientific theories in the world.

The inside of the monument was divided into as many compartments as there were kinds of fruit. The walls were no less than four feet thick. When they were finished, twenty-four ladders were set up, and twenty-four experienced cooks ascended them. These first-class artists were each of them armed with an enormous cooking spoon.

Behind them, on the lower rounds of the ladders, followed the kitchen boys, carrying on their heads pots and pans filled to the brim with jam and sweetmeats, each sort ready to be poured into its destined compartment. This colossal labor was accomplished in one day, and with wonderful exactness.

When the sweetmeats were used to the last drop, when the great spoons had done all their work, the twenty-four cooks descended to earth again. The intrepid Mother Mitchel, who had never quitted the spot, now ascended, followed by the noble Fanfreluche, and dipped her finger into each of the compartments, to assure herself that everything was right.

This part of her duty was not disagreeable, and many

of the scullions would have liked to perform it. But they might have lingered too long over the enchanting task. As for Mother Mitchel, she had been well used to sweets to be excited now. She only wished to do her duty and to insure success.

All went on well. Mother Mitchel had given her approbation. Nothing was needed now but to crown the sublime and delicious edifice by placing upon it the crust—that is, the roof, or dome. This delicate operation was confided to the engineer-in-chief who now showed his superior genius.

The dome, made beforehand of a single piece, was raised in the air by means of twelve balloons whose force of ascension had been carefully calculated. First it was directed, by ropes, exactly over the top of the tart; then at the word of command it gently descended upon the right spot. It was not a quarter of an inch out of place. This was a great triumph for Mother Mitchel and her able assistant.

But all was not over. How should this colossal tart be cooked? That was the question that agitated all the people of the Greedy Country, who came in crowds— lords and commons—to gaze at the wonderful spectacle.

Some of the envious or ill-tempered declared it would be impossible to cook the edifice which Mother Mitchel had built; and the doctors were, no one knows why, the saddest of all.

Mother Mitchel, smiling at the general bewilderment, mounted the summit of the tart; she waved her crutch in the air, and while the cat miaowed in his sweetest voice, suddenly there issued from the woods a vast number of masons, drawing wagons of well-baked bricks, which they had prepared in secret. This sight silenced the ill-wishers and filled the hearts of the Greedy with hope.

In two days an enormous furnace was built around and above the colossal tart, which found itself shut up in an immense earthen pot. Thirty huge mouths, which were connected with thousands of winding pipes for conducting heat all over the building, were soon choked with fuel, by the help of two hundred charcoal burners, who, obeying a private signal, came forth in long array from the forest, each carrying his sack of coal.

Behind them stood Mother Mitchel with a box of matches, ready to fire each oven as it was filled. Of course the kindlings had not been forgotten, and all was soon in a blaze.

When the fire was lighted in the thirty ovens, when they saw the clouds of smoke rolling above the dome, which announced that the cooking had begun, the joy of the people was boundless. Poets improvised odes, and musicians sang verses without end, in honor of the superb prince who had been inspired to feed his people in so dainty a manner, when other rulers could not give them enough even of dry bread.

The names of Mother Mitchel and of the illustrious engineer were not forgotten in their great glorification. Next to His Majesty, they were certainly the first of mankind, and their names were worthy of going down with his to the remotest posterity.

All the envious ones were thunderstruck. They tried to console themselves by saying that the work was not yet finished, and that an accident might happen at the last moment. But they did not really believe a word of this. Notwithstanding all their efforts to look cheerful, it had to be acknowledged that the cooking was possible. Their last resource was to declare the tart a bad one, but that would be biting off their own noses. As for declining to eat it, envy could never go so far as that in the country of the Greedy.

After two days, the unerring nose of Mother Mitchel discovered that the tart was cooked to perfection. The whole country was perfumed with its delicious aroma. Nothing more remained but to take down the furnaces.

Mother Mitchel made her official announcement to His Majesty, who was delighted, and complimented her upon her punctuality. One day was still wanting to complete the month. During this time the people gave their eager help to the engineer in the demolition, wishing to have a hand in the great national work and to hasten the blessed moment.

In the twinkling of an eye the thing was done. The bricks were taken down one by one, counted carefully, and carried into the forest again, to serve for another occasion.

The TART, unveiled, appeared at last in all its majesty and splendor. The dome was gilded, and reflected the rays of the sun in the most dazzling manner. The wildest excitement and rapture ran through the land of the Greedy.

Each one sniffed with open nostrils the appetizing perfume. Their mouths watered, their eyes filled with tears, they embraced, pressed each other's hands, and indulged in touching pantomimes. Then the people of town and country, united by one rapturous feeling, joined hands and danced in a ring around the grand confection.

No one dared to touch the tart before the arrival of His Majesty. Meanwhile, something must be done to allay the universal impatience, and they resolved to show Mother Mitchel the gratitude with which all hearts were filled. She was crowned with the laurel of *conquerors,* which is also the laurel of *sauce,* thus serving a double purpose.

Then they placed her, with her crutch and her cat, upon a sort of throne, and carried her all around her vast work. Before her marched all the musicians of the town, dancing, drumming, fifing, and tooting upon all instruments, while behind her pressed an enthusiastic crowd, who rent the air with their plaudits and filled it with a shower of caps. Her fame was complete, and a noble pride shone on her countenance.

The royal procession arrived. A grand stairway had been built, so that the King and his ministers could mount to the summit of this monumental tart. Thence the King, amid a deep silence, thus addressed his people!

"My children," said he, "you adore tarts. You despise all other food. If you could, you would even eat tarts in your sleep. Very well. Eat as much as you like. Here is one big enough to satisfy you. But know this, that while there remains a single crumb of this august tart, from the height of which I am proud to look down on you, all other food is forbidden you on pain of death.

"While you are here, I have ordered all the pantries to be emptied, and all the butchers, bakers, pork and milk dealers, and fishmongers to shut up their shops. Why leave them open? Why, indeed! Have you not here at discretion what you love best, and enough to last you ever, ever so long? Devote yourselves to it with all your hearts. I do not wish you to be bored with the sight of any other food.

"Greedy ones, behold your TART!"

What enthusiastic applause, what frantic hurrahs rent the air, in answer to this eloquent speech from the throne!

"Long live the King, Mother Mitchel, and her cat! Long live the tart! Down with soup! Down with bread! To the bottom of the sea with all beefsteaks, mutton chops, and roasts!"

Such cries came from every lip. Old men gently stroked their chops, children patted their little stomachs, the crowd licked its thousand lips with eager joy. Even the babies danced in their nurses' arms, so precocious was the passion for tarts in this singular country.

Grave professors, skipping like kids, declaimed Latin

verses in honor of His Majesty and Mother Mitchel and
the shyest young girls opened their mouths like the
beaks of little birds.

As for the doctors, they felt a joy beyond expression.
They had reflected. They understood. But—my friends!—

At last the signal was given. A detachment of the engineer corps arrived, armed with pick and cutlass, and
marched in good order to the assault. A breach was soon
opened, and the distribution began. The King smiled at
the opening of the tart; though vast, it hardly showed
more than a mouse hole in the monstrous wall.

The King stroked his beard grandly. "All goes well,"
said he, "for him who knows how to wait."

Who can tell how long the feast would have lasted
if the King had not given his command that it should
cease? Once more they expressed their gratitude with
cries so stifled that they resembled grunts, and then
rushed to the river.

Never had a nation been so besmeared. Some were
daubed to the eyes, others had their ears and hair all
sticky. As for the little ones, they were marmalade from
head to foot. When they had finished their toilets, the
river ran all red and yellow and was sweetened for several
hours, to the great surprise of all the fishes.

Before returning home, the people presented themselves before the King to receive his commands.

"Children," said he, "the feast will begin again exactly
at six o'clock. Give time to wash the dishes and change
the tablecloths, and you may once more give yourselves

over to pleasure. You shall feast twice a day as long as the tart lasts. Do not forget. Yes! if there is not enough in this one, I will even order ANOTHER from Mother Mitchel; for you know the great woman is indefatigable. Your happiness is my only aim." (Marks of universal joy and emotions.)

"You understand? Noon, and six o'clock! There is no need for me to say be punctual! Go, then, my children —be happy!"

The second feast was as gay as the first, and as long. A pleasant walk in the suburbs—first exercise—then a nap, had refreshed their appetites and unlimbered their jaws. But the King fancied that the breach made in the tart was a little smaller than that of the morning.

" 'Tis well!" said he. " 'Tis well! Wait till tomorrow, my friends; yes, till day after tomorrow, and *next week!*"

The next day the feast still went on gaily; yet at the evening meal the King noticed some empty seats.

"Why is this?" said he with pretended indifference to the court physician.

"Your Majesty," said the great Olibriers, "a few weak stomachs; that is all."

On the next day there were larger empty spaces. The enthusiasm visibly abated. The eighth day the crowd had diminished one-half; the ninth, three-quarters; the tenth day, of the thousand who came at first only two hundred remained; on the eleventh day only one hundred; and on the twelfth—alas! who would have thought it?—a single one answered to the call. Truly he was big enough. His body resembled a hogshead, his mouth an oven, and his lips—we dare not say what. He was known in the town by the name of Patapouf.

They dug out a fresh lump for him from the middle of the tart. It quickly vanished in his vast interior, and he retired with great dignity, proud to maintain the honor of his name and the glory of the Greedy Kingdom.

But the next day, even he, the very last, appeared no more. The unfortunate Patapouf had succumbed, and, like all the other inhabitants of the country, was in a very bad way. In short, it was soon known that the whole town had suffered agonies that night from too much tart.

Let us draw a veil over those hours of torture. Mother Mitchel was in despair. Those ministers who had not guessed the secret dared not open their lips. All the city was one vast hospital. No one was seen in the streets but doctors and apothecaries' boys, running from house to house in frantic haste.

It was dreadful! Dr. Olibriers was nearly knocked out. As for the King, he held his tongue and shut himself up in his palace, but a secret joy shone in his eyes, to the wonder of everyone. He waited three days without a word.

The third day the King said to his ministers:

"Let us now go and see how my poor people are doing, and feel their pulse a little."

The good King went to every house, without forgetting a single one. He visited small and great, rich and poor.

"Oh, oh! Your Majesty," said all, "the tart was good, but may we never see it again! Plague on that tart! Better were dry bread. Your Majesty, for mercy's sake, a little dry bread! Oh, a morsel of dry bread, how good it would be!"

"No, indeed," replied the King. *"There is more of that tart!"*

"What! Your Majesty, *must* we eat it all?"

"You *must!*" sternly replied the King. "You MUST! By the immortal beefsteaks! Not one of you shall have a slice of bread, and not a loaf shall be baked in the kingdom while there remains a crumb of that excellent tart!"

"What misery!" thought these poor people. "That tart forever!"

The sufferers were in despair. There was only one cry through all the town: "Ow! ow! ow!" For even the strongest and most courageous were in horrible agonies. They twisted, they writhed, they lay down, they got up. Always the inexorable colic. The dogs were not happier than their masters; even they had had too much tart.

The spiteful tart looked in at all the windows. Built upon a height, it commanded the town. The mere sight of it made everybody ill, and its former admirers had nothing but curses for it now. Unhappily, nothing they could say or do made it any smaller; still formidable, it was a frightful joke for those miserable mortals.

Most of them buried their heads in their pillows, drew their nightcaps over their eyes, and lay in bed all day to shut out the sight of it. But this would not do; they knew, they felt it was there. It was a nightmare, a horrible burden, a torturing anxiety.

In the midst of this terrible consternation the King remained inexorable during eight days. His heart bled for his people, but the lesson must sink deep if it were to bear fruit in future. When their pains were cured, little by little, through fasting alone, and his subjects pronounced these trembling words, "We are hungry!" the King sent them trays laden with—the inevitable tart.

"Ah!" cried they, with anguish, "the tart again! Always the tart, and nothing but the tart! Better were death!"

A few, who were almost famished, shut their eyes, and tried to eat a bit of the detested food; but it was all in vain—they could not swallow a mouthful.

At length came the happy day when the King, thinking their punishment had been severe enough and could never be forgotten, believed them at length cured of their greediness.

That day he ordered Mother Mitchel to make in one of her colossal pots a super-excellent soup, of which a bowl was sent to every family. They received it with as much rapture as the Hebrews did the manna in the desert. They would gladly have had twice as much, but after their long fast it would not have been prudent. It was a proof that they had learned something already, that they understood this.

The next day, more soup. This time the King allowed

slices of bread with it. How much this good soup comforted all the town! The next day there was a little more bread with it and a little soup meat. Then for a few days the kind Prince gave them roast beef and vegetables. The cure was complete.

The joy over this new diet was as great as ever had been felt for the tart. It promised to last longer. They were sure to sleep soundly, and to wake refreshed. It was pleasant to see in every house tables surrounded with happy, rosy faces and laden with good nourishing food.

The Greedy people never fell back into their old ways. Their once puffed-out, sallow faces shone with health; they became, not fat, but muscular, ruddy, and solid.

The butchers and bakers reopened their shops; the pastry cooks and confectioners shut theirs. The Country of the Greedy was turned upside down, and if it kept its name, it was only from habit. As for the tart, it was not forgotten.

Today, in that marvelous country, there cannot be found a paper of sugar plums or a basket of cakes. It is charming to see the red lips and beautiful teeth of the people. If they still have a king, he may well be proud to be their ruler.

Does this story teach that tarts and pies should never be eaten? No; but there is reason in all things.

The doctors alone did not profit by this great revolution. They could not afford to drink wine any longer in a land where indigestion had become unknown. The apothecaries were no less unhappy, spiders sun webs over their windows, and their horrible remedies were no longer of use.

Ask no more about Mother Mitchel. She was ridiculed without measure by those who had adored her. To complete her misfortune, she lost her cat. Alas for Mother Mitchel!

The King received the reward of his wisdom. His grateful people called him neither Charles the Bold, nor Peter the Terrible, nor Louis the Great, but always by the noble name of Prosper I, the Reasonable.

Indian Children Long Ago

Nancy Byrd Turner

Where we play in field and hill,
　Running high and low,
Other children used to play,
　Long and long ago.

Little Indians straight and slim,
　Boys with belt and feather,
Little girls with colored beads,
　Playing all together.

Laughing, calling through our yard
　(When 'twas field of maize),
Swift and light they used to run,
　Back in other days;

Through our garden (once a wood)
   In and out again,
Past the house they ran, and back—
   'Twas a wigwam then.

Sometimes when the air is clear,
   On a quiet day,
We can almost hear them still,
   Shouting at their play!

A Basket for Thanksgiving

Carolyn Sherwin Bailey

The Farmer twins, Susan and Eliphalet, hung over the stair railing and peered down upon the gay scene of the husking bee. It was the week before Thanksgiving in old Boscawen, New Hampshire. Susan and Eliphalet were children of our homespun days, and the harvest season, when the corn was stripped of husks and shelled, was one of the year's holidays.

All the young people of the village were gathered in the Farmers' great kitchen, making merry as they piled baskets full of yellow kernels and heaped huge piles of corn husks.

It was like looking down upon a stage. The kitchen, now that the short November day was darkening into late afternoon, was bright with candles set in tin holders that Susan had polished to silver brightness. The pitch-pine knots that Eliphalet had gathered in the woods be-

yond the Hollow flamed crimson. Two pumpkin jack-
o'-lanterns carved by the twins sat grinning on the shelf
over the fireplace, among pewter mugs and plates.

On the sideboard there was spread the feast which
Susan and her mother had made ready. The Dutch oven
beside the fireplace had been full for days. Hasty pudding to be eaten with rich golden molasses. Earthen pots
of hot baked beans. Fried apple turnovers. Doughnuts.
Gingerbread and yellow cheese. Apple pies. Pumpkin
pies.

A pleasant hum of talk came up to the children, accompanied by the rasping sound of the ears of corn
rubbed against the sharp handles of tin frying pans,
brought by the guests to save their fingers in the corn
husking.

In a corner of the kitchen near the fireplace, leaning
against one of the corn shocks brought in for decoration,
an odd figure of a man was curled up.

"Nathan sleeps," Susan said, pointing to the visitor
who wore a faded Indian blanket, moccasins, and homespun breeches. "All he came for was to beg corn husks
left from the husking to make his baskets."

"Those who do not work must expect to suffer,"
Eliphalet observed piously. "We have heard Deacon
Little say that often enough in meeting."

Susan's forehead wrinkled in thought. "But Nathan
Hunt does work," she said. "The baskets he weaves are
honestly made and very useful. They do say there is no
better basketmaker this side of Boston."

"He has done no husking," her brother insisted stub-

bornly, "while our fingers are sore from the sharp kernels. There he sleeps waiting to be roused for his supper.
One, two, three, go!" And down from the stairs, plump
on the old basketmaker's head, fell the overripe pumpkin that Eliphalet had saved for this prank. It burst. The
basketmaker was covered with pulp, seeds, and confusion.

In a burst of laughter, for husking time was an occasion for pranks, Nathan disappeared, leaving a trail of
orange pumpkin on the freshly sanded kitchen floor, out
into the twilight, and toward the Hollow.

"For shame! Who played this unkind joke?" Mistress
Farmer asked. "Nathan Hunt brought me this morning
one of the finest woven baskets for sifting grain that I
ever saw."

But the twins slipped down into the crowded kitchen
without being caught. Susan hastened to pass plates for
the husking feast, and Eliphalet had a sudden errand out
to the woodshed to bring in more logs for the fire. Just
then the fiddlers who were to play for dances after supper
arrived, and someone began singing. The old basketmaker was forgotten, and the fun that followed the day's
husking began.

Not altogether forgotten, though. As Susan piled a
platter with doughnuts, she touched her little brown
sewing basket that stood on the dresser. Nathan Hunt
had made the basket for her, that she might carry her
pincushion, needles, and thimble in it to a quilting bee,
or spend a happy evening at home sewing for her dolls
in the candlelight.

Willow splints and fragrant rushes from Mill Brook,

sweetly scented with the pine needles that Nathan had woven in for decoration, made the little workbasket. The feel of it touched Susan's warm heart. She beckoned to Eliphalet, who was trying to husk a few leftover ears of corn, unobserved, behind the settle.

"Which would you rather do, Eliphalet Farmer? Eat your supper on the road or take the birching that awaits you? Our mother's eyes are sharp and she knows who dropped that squashy pumpkin on Nathan Hunt. I have a mind to take Nathan's husking supper to him. There is time before the husking bee is over. And if we are both away on such an errand, you may avert the rod and I a tongue-lashing."

"I will go with you," the boy decided.

It took but a moment to put some food in their pockets, and wrap an apple turnover, some cheese, and doughnuts in a linen cloth. Eliphalet gathered up the bunch of corn husks that the basketmaker had dropped in his hasty departure. Susan put on her bonnet and cape and Eliphalet his warm cap. His thick tow shirt, homespun, cassimere clothes, and buckskin leggings were protection from almost any weather.

Mistress Farmer, busily serving the huskers, did not see the twins as they slipped out of the kitchen. In a few moments they had left the Plain, where they lived, and had dipped down into a darkening north road that led into Boscawen's Hollow, the Valley of Industry.

In the daytime the Hollow rattled and clashed and banged. There the town sawmill and the flour mill hummed, their great wheels turned by the rushing flow of Mill Brook. From the Hollow, on the swift currents of the Merrimac River, hundreds of pine masts, spars, and bowsprits floated down to Lowell and Boston for the shipyards that launched vessels sailing to the Indies and China. There in the Hollow rang the coopers's hammers making staves and iron hoops for the barrels that traveled on flatboats to Boston, to hold molasses, sugar, and beef.

The Boscawen boys and girls loved the Hollow. There they could sail boats on the brook, gather blocks of wood for their building, and go nutting in the forest from which came the sweet-smelling logs of pine, white and red oak, poplar, hemlock, and chestnut that were shaped and turned into ships' spars at the sawmill.

But the valley now was still. With the dropping of the sun behind Clay Hill, which lifted its wooded peak west of the Hollow, the mill wheels rested, forge fires burned out to ashes, and the Valley of Industry was given over to the wild creatures that hid in the forest by day.

"There is a price for a wolf pelt posted on the meeting-house door. Two shillings," Eliphalet said as they trudged along through the dusk. "I would have been wise to bring along a musket."

"Oh!" Susan gasped. "Why speak of wolves? Hark!"

The dry grass and bushes behind them rustled with padded footsteps. Susan gripped her brother's arm. He looked back, straight into two great gleaming eyes.

"A wolf is following us. Run!" he said. The two sped on, losing the path in the darkness, finding it again, panting, always pursued by the stealthy four-footed steps. They ran pell-mell into a man in front of the sawmill who was as surprised as they.

The lantern that burned in the mill window all night showed that they had overtaken Thomas Courser, the village herb man, on his way home to his cottage in the forest. Thomas's basket of thyme, summer savory, mint, and sage flavored tasty stuffing for roasted ducks and turkeys. The children of Boscawen were dosed with his home-made medicines and blistered with his mustard plasters. Everyone knew him.

"Thomas, good Thomas, save us!" Susan gasped. "We are pursued by wolves."

Thomas peered into the dark road. Then he chuckled. "Puss! Puss!" he called, and a great black cat came purring out of the darkness and rubbed against his legs. Behind came another cat and another. Thomas Courser threw them some sprigs of catnip from his basket. "They are the flour-mill tabbies," he said. "They must be about their mousing all day, but when I start home they will follow me a mile for a sprig of catnip. Where are you bound for at suppertime?"

Eliphalet was too ashamed to reply, thinking how he had run away from a mill puss. Susan explained.

"Well, good night and good luck," said Thomas, the herb man, as they reached the turnpike where he must leave them. "Nathan Hunt well deserves the feast you are bringing him." Soon he was only a fading shadow, a passing fragrance of mint and catnip carried by the night wind. The twins went on, Susan with her basket of food, Eliphalet with his corn husks, their free hands tightly clasped.

Once more they were startled by animals' footsteps in a field. They turned out to be only Deacon Little's flock of French merino sheep, crunching their supper of late grass. A little farther along the turnpike road they jumped, and their hearts beat faster as a menacing skeleton of a creature raised its arms to stop them. But they had just passed the shop of Tristram Noyes, who made farm tools by hand for Boscawen and the neighboring villages. What had frightened the twins was only one of Tristram's half-finished plows at the edge of the road.

A golden harvest moon rose at last to show them their way. They laughed and waved at the jolly man in the moon. An echo joined them for company until they came to the end of the road. There under the shadow of Clay Hill the twins saw candlelight spreading a narrow path to guide them.

They ran on and came to the cottage shop of Nathan Hunt, the Boscawen basketmaker. Eliphalet rapped at the door, and when it opened, Susan held out her package of goodies. "We beg your pardon for dropping an overripe pumpkin on your head, Nathan," she said.

"It was I who did it, not Susan," Eliphalet said honestly. "And it was Susan as well who packed this supper for you and was minded that we come and beg your pardon."

The basketmaker chuckled. Then he laughed until

the forest gave back his ringing laughter. He had removed all traces of pumpkin from his person, and his frugal meal of hominy and milk was on his table. It was said in Boscawen that Nathan Hunt grew plump on laughter. He was a poor man, but his cheery chuckles, as he went from house to house peddling his baskets, were as welcome as his wares. He laid out two more wooden plates as Susan opened the food they had brought.

"That pumpkin was a husking joke," he said. "I understood that you would not play such a trick on an old man except the occasion gave you the liberty. Draw up and share these good things. I know that Mistress Farmer's turnovers and doughnuts are not to be equaled in the village."

As the three ate in the candlelight, the children looked around the little cottage, crowded to the corners with Nathan Hunt's rushes, hickory and ash splints, willow reeds, and the golden corn husks that Eliphalet had brought.

Sunny days the old basketmaker spent in the woods or along the brook, searching for the young trees which he would chop into basket lengths to be shaved down into splints. Rainy or winter days he polished his splints, made the hoops that fitted together and shaped the basket rim, the bottom, and the handle, and then wove the basket with skilled fingers that had learned their art from the Indians.

There was daily need for Nathan Hunt's baskets: for gathering apples, sifting grain, straining yellow curd before it was put in the cheese press, for holding the balls of bright yarn that Mistress Farmer and the other mothers of the village knitted into mittens and mufflers and stockings, for filling with nuts in the autumn. They were long-lived baskets that Nathan Hunt made, and he gave them beautiful patterns of corn-husk braiding, designs worked in pine needles, and slender willow borders like lace.

"You do forgive us, Nathan?" Susan asked between bites of a doughnut.

The old basketmaker laughed again. They had finished supper, and Nathan brought out a big hickory basket as round as a melon and woven so well that it seemed of one piece.

"I like a prank myself," he said. "But this you must do in penance. Here is a stout basket that will last a lifetime and longer. Use it for a Thanksgiving basket, to hold the fruits of the harvest, and to carry food to those who need it. Then I shall never think again that you tried to turn me into a scarecrow. I will lend you my lantern to light you home. Be off now, for the evening is on us and your mother will worry. Good-by and a good Thanksgiving Day!"

As Susan and Eliphalet started home, they could see for a long distance the light of the basketmaker's candle. When it was gone, the lantern made a bright path that guided them. When they came to their house, the huskers were still making merry, playing games and singing to the fiddlers' music. Their mother tried to look stern, but when the twins explained where they had been, all she did was give them each a plump square of pumpkin pie.

"You did well to ask Nathan Hunt's pardon for your mischief," she said. "We could hardly keep house or farm without his baskets."

That was a long time ago, for Nathan Hunt lived and worked in the little New Hampshire village of Boscawen about the year 1840. His name has come down to us as that of a basketmaker whose work was so carefully and beautifully done that it made history.

Harvesting, preparing the grain for the miller, cheese-making, sewing, knitting, all our patiently wrought handcrafts were woven into the polished forest-scented splints of Nathan Hunt's baskets. The children loved his basketry cradles for dolls, his school lunch baskets with stout covers, his little sewing baskets that held patchwork squares, his baskets for young fishermen.

Machines today have taken away the work of the basketmaker, but we find his handicraft treasured in museums beside that of the Indians. And each Thanksgiving Day we may remember him as we fill a basket for someone who needs it.

A Thanksgiving Dinner
That Flew Away

Hezekiah Butterworth

"Honk!"

I spun around like a top, looking nervously in every direction. I was familiar with that sound; I had heard it before, during two summer vacations, at the old farmhouse on the Cape.

It had been a terror to me. I always put a door, a fence, or a stone wall between me and that sound as speedily as possible.

I had just come down from the city to the Cape for my third summer vacation. I had left the car with my arms full of bundles, and hurried toward Aunt Targood's.

The cottage stood in from the road. There was a long meadow in front of it. In the meadow were two great oaks and some clusters of lilacs. An old, mossy stone wall protected the grounds from the road, and a long walk ran from the old wooden gate to the door.

148

It was a sunny day, and my heart was light. The orioles were flaming in the old orchards; the bobolinks were tossing themselves about in the long meadows of timothy, daisies, and patches of clover. There was a scent of new-mown hay in the air.

In the distance lay the bay, calm and resplendent, with white sails and specks of boats. Beyond it rose Martha's Vineyard, green and cool and bowery, and at its wharf lay a steamer.

I was, as I said, lighthearted. I was thinking of rides over the sandy roads at the close of the long, bright days; of excursions on the bay; of clambakes and picnics.

I was hungry; and before me rose visions of Aunt Targood's fish dinners, roast chickens, berry pies. I was thirsty; but ahead was the old well sweep, and, behind the cool lattice of the dairy window, were pans of milk in abundance.

I tripped on toward the door with light feet, lugging my bundles and beaded with perspiration, but unmindful of all discomforts in the thought of the bright days and good things in store for me.

"Honk! Honk!"

My heart gave a bound!

Where did that sound come from?

Out of a cool cluster of innocent-looking lilac bushes I saw a dark object cautiously moving. It seemed to have no head. I knew, however, that it had a head. I had seen it; it had seized me once on the previous summer, and I had been in terror of it during all the rest of the season.

I looked down into the irregular grass, and saw the head and a very long neck running along on the ground, propelled by the dark body, like a snake running away from a ball. It was coming toward me, and faster and faster as it approached.

I dropped all my bundles.

In a few flying leaps I returned to the road again, and armed myself with a stick from a pile of cordwood.

"Honk! Honk! Honk!"

It was a call of triumph. The head was high in the air now. My enemy moved grandly forward, as became the monarch of the great meadow farmyard.

I stood with beating heart after my retreat.

It was Aunt Targood's gander.

How he enjoyed his triumph, and how small and cowardly he made me feel!

"Honk! Honk! Honk!"

The geese came out of the lilac bushes, bowing their heads to him in admiration. Then came the goslings—a long procession of awkward, half-feathered things: they appeared equally delighted.

The gander seemed to be telling his admiring audience all about it: how a strange girl with many bundles had attempted to cross the yard; how he had driven her back, and had captured her bundles, and now was monarch of the field. He clapped his wings when he had finished his heroic story, and sent forth such a "honk!" as might have startled a major general.

Then he, with an air of great dignity and coolness, began to examine my baggage.

Among my effects were several pounds of chocolate caramels done up in brown paper. Aunt Targood liked caramels, and I had brought her a large supply.

He tore off the wrappers quickly. Bit one. It was good. He began to distribute the bonbons among the geese, and they, with much liberality and good will, among the goslings.

This was too much. I ventured through the gate swinging my cordwood stick.

"*Shoo!*"

He dropped his head on the ground, and drove it down the walk in a lively waddle toward me.

"*Shoo!*"

It was Aunt Targood's voice at the door.

He stopped immediately.

His head was in the air again.

"*Shoo!*"

Out came Aunt Targood with her broom.

She always corrected the gander with her broom. If I were to be whipped I should choose a broom—not the stick.

As soon as he beheld the broom he retired, although with much offended pride and dignity, to the lilac bushes; and the geese and goslings followed him.

"Hester, you dear child, come here. I was expecting you, and had been looking out for you, but missed sight of you. I had forgotten all about the gander."

We gathered up the bundles and the caramels. I was lighthearted again.

How cool was the sitting room, with the woodbine

falling about the open windows! Aunt brought me a pitcher of milk and some strawberries, some bread and honey, and a fan.

While I was resting and taking my lunch, I could hear the gander discussing the affairs of the farmyard with the geese. I did not greatly enjoy the discussion. His tone of voice was very proud, and he did not seem to be speaking well of me. I was suspicious that he did not think me a very brave girl. A young person likes to be spoken well of, even by the gander.

Aunt Targood's gander had been the terror of many well-meaning people, and of some evildoers, for many years. I have seen tramps and pack peddlers enter the gate, and start on toward the door, when there would sound that ringing warning like a war blast. "Honk! Honk!" and in a few minutes these unwelcome people would be gone.

Farmhouse boarders from the city would sometimes enter the yard, thinking to draw water by the old well sweep: in a few minutes it was customary to hear shrieks, and to see women and children flying over the walls, followed by air-rending "honks!" and jubilant cackles from the victorious gander and his admiring family.

"Aunt, what makes you keep that gander, year after year?" said I, one evening, as we were sitting on the lawn before the door. "Is it because he is a kind of a watchdog, and keeps troublesome people away?"

"No, child, no; I do not wish to keep most people away, not well-behaved people, nor to distress nor annoy anyone. The fact is, there is a story about that gander that I do not like to speak of to everyone—something that makes me feel tender toward him, so that if he needs a whipping, I would rather do it. He knows something that no one else knows. I could not have him killed or sent away. You have heard me speak of Nathaniel, my oldest boy?"

"Yes."

"That is his picture in my room, you know. He was a good boy to me. He loved his mother. I loved Nathaniel —you cannot think how much I loved Nathaniel. It was on my account that he went away.

"The farm did not produce enough for us all: Nathaniel, John, and I. We worked hard and had a hard time. One year—that was ten years ago—we were sued for our taxes.

" 'Nathaniel,' said I, 'I will go to taking boarders.'

"Then he looked up to me and said:

" 'Mother, I will go to sea.'

" 'Where?' asked I, in surprise.

" 'In a coaster.'

"I turned white. How I felt!

" 'You and John can manage the place,' he continued. 'One of the vessels sails next week—Uncle Aaron's; he offers to take me.'

"It seemed best, and he made preparations to go.

"The spring before Skipper Ben—you have met Skipper Ben—had given me some goose eggs; he had brought them from Canada, and said that they were wild-goose eggs.

"I set them under hens. In four weeks I had three goslings. I took them into the house at first, but afterward made a pen for them out in the yard. I brought them up myself, and one of those goslings is that gander.

"Skipper Ben came over to see me the day before Nathaniel was to sail. Aaron came with him.

"I said to Aaron:

" 'What can I give to Nathaniel to carry to sea with him to make him think of home? Cake, preserves, apples? I haven't got much; I have done all I can for him, poor boy.'

"Brother looked at me curiously, and said:

" 'Give him one of those wild geese, and we will fatten it on shipboard and will have it for our Thanksgiving dinner.'

"What brother Aaron said pleased me. The young gander was a noble bird, the handsomest of the lot; and I resolved to keep the geese to kill for my own use and to give *him* to Nathaniel.

"The next morning—it was late in September—I took leave of Nathaniel. I tried to be calm and cheerful and hopeful. I watched him as he went down the walk with the gander struggling under his arms.

"A stranger would have laughed, but I did not feel like laughing; it was true that the boys who went coasting were usually gone but a few months and came home hardy and happy. But when poverty compels a mother and son to part, after they have been true to each other, and shared their feelings in common, it seems hard, it seems hard—although I do not like to murmur or complain at anything allotted to me.

"I saw him go over the hill. On the top he stopped and held up the gander. He disappeared; yes, my own Nathaniel disappeared. I think of him now as one who disappeared.

"November came—it was a terrible month on the coast that year. Storm followed storm; the seafaring people talked constantly of wrecks and losses. I could not sleep on the nights of those high winds. I used to lie awake thinking over all the happy hours I had lived with Nathaniel.

"Thanksgiving week came.

"It was full of an Indian-summer brightness after the long storms. The nights were frosty, bright, and calm.

"I could sleep on those calm nights.

"One morning I thought I heard a strange sound in the woodland pasture. It was like a wild goose. I listened; it was repeated. I was lying in bed. I started up—I thought I had been dreaming.

"On the night before Thanksgiving I went to bed early, being very tired. The moon was full; the air was calm and still. I was thinking of Nathaniel, and I wondered if he would indeed have the gander for his Thanksgiving dinner: if it would be cooked as well as I would have cooked it, and if he would think of me that day.

"I was just going to sleep, when suddenly I heard a sound that make me start up and hold my breath.

" '*Honk!*'

"I thought it was a dream followed by a nervous shock.

" '*Honk! Honk!*'

"There it was again, in the yard. I was surely awake and in my senses.

"I heard the geese cackle.

" '*Honk! Honk! Honk!*'

"I got out of bed and lifted the curtain. It was almost as light as day. Instead of two geese there were three. Had one of the neighbors' geese stolen away?

"I should have thought so, and should not have felt disturbed, but for the reason that none of the neighbors' geese had that peculiar call—that hornlike tone that I had noticed in mine.

"I went out of the door.

"The *third* goose looked like the very gander I had given Nathaniel. Could it be?

"I did not sleep. I rose early and went to the crib for some corn.

"It *was* a gander—a 'wild' gander—that had come in the night. He seemed to know me.

"I trembled all over as though I had seen a ghost. I was so faint that I sat down on the meal chest.

"As I was in that place, a bill pecked against the door. The door opened. The strange gander came hobbling over the crib stone and went to the corncrib. He stopped there, looked at me, and gave a sort of glad 'honk,' as though he knew me and was glad to see me.

"I was certain that he was the gander I had raised

and that Nathaniel had lifted into the air when he gave me his last recognition from the top of the hill.

"It overcame me. It was Thanksgiving. The church bell would soon be ringing as on Sunday. And here was Nathaniel's Thanksgiving dinner, and brother Aaron's. Had it flown away? Where was the vessel?

"Years have passed—ten. You know I waited and waited for my boy to come back. December grew dark with its rainy seas; the snows fell; May lighted up the hills, but the vessel never came back. Nathaniel—my Nathaniel—never returned.

"That gander knows something he could tell me if he could talk. Birds have memories. *He* remembered the corncrib—he remembered something else. I wish he *could* talk, poor bird! I wish he could talk. I will never sell him, nor kill him, nor have him abused. *He knows!*"

The Pumpkin Giant

Mary Wilkins Freeman

A very long time ago, before our grandmother's time, or our great-grandmother's, there were no pumpkins; people had never eaten a pumpkin pie, or even stewed pumpkin; and that was the time when the Pumpkin Giant flourished.

There have been a great many giants who have flourished since the world began, and although a select few of them have been good giants, the majority of them have been so bad that their crimes even more than their size have gone to make them notorious. But the Pumpkin Giant was an uncommonly bad one, and his general appearance and his behavior were such as to make one shudder to an extent that you would hardly believe possible.

The convulsive shivering caused by the mere mention of his name, and, in some cases where the people were unusually sensitive, by the mere thought of him even, more resembled the blue ague than anything else; indeed, it was known by the name of "the Giant's Shakes."

The Pumpkin Giant was very tall; he probably would have overtopped most of the giants you have ever heard of. I don't suppose the Giant who lived on the Bean-stalk whom Jack visited was anything to compare with him; nor that it would have been a possible thing for the Pumpkin Giant, had he received an invitation to spend an afternoon with the Bean-stalk Giant, to accept, on account of his inability to enter the Bean-stalk Giant's door, no matter how much he stooped.

The Pumpkin Giant had a very large yellow head, which was also smooth and shiny. His eyes were big and round, and glowed like coals of fire; and you would almost have thought that his head was lit up inside with candles. Indeed there was a rumor to that effect among the common people, but that was all nonsense, of course; no one of the more enlightened class credited it for an instant. His mouth, which stretched half around his head, was furnished with rows of pointed teeth, and he was never known to hold it any other way than wide open.

The Pumpkin Giant lived in a castle, as a matter of course; it is not fashionable for a giant to live in any other kind of a dwelling—why, nothing would be more tame and uninteresting than a giant in a two-story white house with green blinds and a picket fence, or even a brown-stone front, if he could get into either of them, which he could not.

The Giant's castle was situated on a mountain, as it ought to have been, and there was also the usual court-yard before it, and the customary moat, which was full of—*bones!* All I have got to say about these bones is, they were not mutton bones. A great many details of this story must be left to the imagination of the reader; they are too harrowing to relate.

The Pumpkin Giant was fonder of little boys and girls than anything else in the world; but he was some-what fonder of little boys, and more particularly of *fat* little boys.

The fear and horror of this Giant extended over the whole country. Even the King on his throne was so severely afflicted with the Giant's Shakes that he had been obliged to have the throne propped, for fear it should topple over in some unusually violent fit.

There was good reason why the King shook: his only daughter, the Princess Ariadne Diana, was probably the fattest princess in the whole world at that date. So fat was she that she had never walked a step in the dozen years of her life, being totally unable to progress over the earth by any method except rolling.

And a really beautiful sight it was, too, to see the Princess Ariadne Diana, in her cloth-of-gold rolling suit, faced with green velvet and edged with ermine, with her glittering crown on her head, trundling along the avenues of the royal gardens, which had been furnished with strips of rich carpeting for her express accommo-dation.

But gratifying as it would have been to the King, her

sire, under other circumstances, to have had such an unusually interesting daughter, it now only served to fill his heart with the greatest anxiety on her account. The Princess was never allowed to leave the palace without a bodyguard of fifty knights, the very flower of the King's troops, with lances in rest, but in spite of all this precaution, the King shook.

Meanwhile among the ordinary people who could not procure an escort of fifty armed knights for the plump among their children, the ravages of the Pumpkin Giant were frightful. It was apprehended at one time that there would be very few fat little girls, and no fat little boys at all, left in the kingdom. And what made matters worse, at that time the Giant commenced taking a tonic to increase his appetite.

Finally the King, in desperation, issued a proclamation that he would knight anyone, be he noble or common, who should cut off the head of the Pumpkin Giant. This was the King's usual method of rewarding any noble deed in his kingdom. It was a cheap method, and besides everybody liked to be a knight.

When the King issued his proclamation every man in the kingdom who was not already a knight straightway tried to contrive ways and means to kill the Pumpkin Giant. But there was one obstacle which seemed insurmountable: they were afraid, and all of them had the Giant's Shakes so badly, that they could not possibly have held a knife steady enough to cut off the Giant's head, even if they had dared to go near enough for that purpose.

There was one man who lived not far from the terrible Giant's castle, a poor man, his only worldly wealth consisting of a large potato field and a cottage in front of it. But he had a boy of twelve, an only son, who rivaled the Princess Ariadne Diana in point of fatness. He was unable to have a bodyguard for his son, so the amount of terror which the inhabitants of that humble cottage suffered day and night was heartrending.

The poor mother had been unable to leave her bed for two years, on account of the Giant's Shakes; her husband barely got a living from the potato field; half the time he and his wife had hardly enough to eat, as it naturally took the larger part of the potatoes to satisfy the fat little boy, their son, and their situation was truly pitiable.

The fat boy's name was Æneas, his father's name was Patroclus, and his mother's Daphne. It was all the fashion in those days to have classical names. And as that was a fashion as easily adopted by the poor as the rich, everybody had them. They were just like Jim and Tommy and May in these days. Why, the Princess's name, Ariadne Diana, was nothing more nor less than Ann Eliza with us.

One morning Patroclus and Æneas were out in the field digging potatoes, for new potatoes were just in the market. The Early Rose potato had not been discovered in those days, but there was another potato, perhaps equally good, which attained to a similar degree of celebrity. It was called the Young Plantagenet, and reached a very large size indeed, much larger than the Early Rose does in our time.

Well, Patroclus and Æneas had just dug perhaps a bushel of Young Plantagenet potatoes. It was slow work with them, for Patroclus had the Giant's Shakes badly that morning, and of course Æneas was not very swift. He rolled about among the potato hills after the manner of the Princess Ariadne Diana; but he did not present as imposing an appearance as she, in his homespun farmer's frock.

All at once the earth trembled violently. Patroclus and Æneas looked up and saw the Pumpkin Giant coming with his mouth wide open. "Get behind me, oh, my darling son!" cried Patroclus.

Æneas obeyed, but it was of no use, for you could see his cheeks each side his father's waistcoat.

Patroclus was not ordinarily a brave man, but he was brave in an emergency; and as that is the only time when there is the slightest need of bravery, it was just as well.

The Pumpkin Giant strode along faster and faster, opening his mouth wider and wider, until they could fairly hear it crack at the corners.

Then Patroclus picked up an enormous Young Plantagenet and threw it plump into the Pumpkin Giant's mouth. The Giant choked and gasped, and choked and gasped, and finally tumbled down and died.

Patroclus and Æneas, while the Giant was choking, had run to the house and locked themselves in; then they looked out of the kitchen window; when they saw the Giant tumble down and lie quite still, they knew he must be dead. Then Daphne was immediately cured of the Giant's Shakes, and got out of bed for the first time in two years. Patroclus sharpened the carving knife on the kitchen stove, and they all went out into the potato field.

They cautiously approached the prostrate Giant, for fear he might be shamming, and might suddenly spring up at them and—Æneas. But no, he did not move at all; he was quite dead. And, all taking turns, they hacked off his head with the carving knife.

The King was notified of the death of the Pumpkin Giant, and was greatly rejoiced thereby. His Giant's Shakes ceased, the props were removed from the throne, and the Princess Ariadne Diana was allowed to go out without her bodyguard of fifty knights, much to her delight, for she found them a great hindrance to the enjoyment of her daily outings.

It was a great cross, not to say an embarrassment, when she was gleefully rolling in pursuit of a charming red-and-gold butterfly to find herself suddenly stopped short by an armed knight with his lance in rest.

But the King, although his gratitude for the noble deed knew no bounds, omitted to give the promised reward and knight Patroclus.

I hardly know how it happened—I don't think it was anything intentional. Patroclus felt rather hurt about it, and Daphne would have liked to be a lady, but Æneas did not care in the least. He had the Giant's head to play with and that was reward enough for him.

There was not a boy in the neighborhood but envied

him his possession of such a unique plaything; and when they would stand looking over the wall of the potato field with longing eyes, and he was flying over the ground with the head, his happiness knew no bounds; and Æneas played so much with the Giant's head that finally late in the fall it got broken and scattered all over the field.

Next spring all over Patroclus's potato field grew running vines, and in the fall Giant's heads. There they were all over the field, hundreds of them! Then there was consternation indeed! The natural conclusion to be arrived at when the people saw the yellow Giant's heads making their appearance above the ground was that the rest of the Giants were coming.

"There was one Pumpkin Giant before," said they, "now there will be a whole army of them. If it was dreadful then what will it be in the future? If one Pumpkin Giant gave us the shakes so badly, what will a whole army of them do?"

But when some time had elapsed and nothing more of the Giants appeared above the surface of the potato field, and as, moreover, the heads had not yet displayed any sign of opening their mouths, the people began to feel a little easier, and the general excitement subsided somewhat, although the King had ordered out Ariadne Diana's bodyguard again.

Now Æneas had been born with a propensity for putting everything into his mouth and tasting it; there was scarcely anything in his vicinity which could by any possibility be tasted which he had not eaten a bit of.

This propensity was so alarming in his babyhood that Daphne purchased a book of antidotes; and if it had not been for her admirable good judgment in doing so, this story would probably never have been told, for no human baby could possibly have survived the diet which Æneas had indulged in. There was scarcely one of the antidotes which had not been resorted to from time to time.

Æneas had become acquainted with the peculiar flavor of almost everything in his immediate vicinity except the Giant's heads; and he naturally enough cast longing eyes at them. Night and day he wondered what a Giant's head could taste like, till finally one day when Patroclus was away he stole out into the potato field, cut a bit out of one of the Giant's heads, and ate it. He was almost afraid to, but he reflected that his mother could give him an antidote, so he ventured.

It tasted very sweet and nice; he liked it so much that he cut off another piece and ate that, then another and another, until he had eaten two-thirds of a Giant's head. Then he thought it was about time for him to go in and tell his mother and take an antidote, although he did not feel ill at all yet.

"Mother," said he, rolling slowly into the cottage, "I have eaten two-thirds of a Giant's head, and I guess you had better give me an antidote."

"Oh, my precious son," cried Daphne, "how could you?" She looked in her book of antidotes, but could not find one antidote for a Giant's head.

"Oh, Æneas, my dear, dear son," groaned Daphne,

"there is no antidote for Giant's head! What shall we do?"

Then she sat down and wept, and Æneas wept, too, as loud as he possibly could. And he apparently had excellent reason to, for it did not seem possible that a boy could eat two-thirds of a Giant's head and survive it without an antidote.

Patroclus came home, and they told him, and he sat down and lamented with them.

All day they sat down and wept and watched Æneas, expecting every moment to see him die. But he did not die; on the contrary, he had never felt so well in his life.

Finally at sunset Æneas looked up and laughed. "I am not going to die," said he; "I never felt so well; you had better stop crying. And I am going out to get some more of that Giant's head; I am hungry."

"Don't, don't!" cried his father and mother, but he went, for he generally took his own way, very like most only sons. He came back with a whole Giant's head in his arms.

"See here, Father and Mother," cried he; "we'll all have some of this; it evidently is not poison, and it is good—a great deal better than potatoes!"

Patroclus and Daphne hesitated, but they were hungry, too. Since the crop of Giant's heads had sprung up in their field instead of potatoes, they had been hungry most of the time, so they tasted.

"It is good," said Daphne, "but I think it would be better cooked."

So she put some in a kettle of water over the fire, and let it boil awhile; then she dished it up, and they all ate it. It was delicious. It tasted more like stewed pumpkin than anything else; in fact, it was stewed pumpkin.

Daphne was inventive and something of a genius, and next day she concocted another dish out of the Giant's heads. She boiled them, and sifted them, and mixed them with eggs and sugar and milk and spice; then she lined some plates with puff paste, filled them with the mixture, and set them in the oven to bake.

The result was unparalleled; nothing half so exquisite had ever been tasted. They were all in ecstasies, Æneas in particular. They gathered all the Giant's heads and stored them in the cellar. Daphne baked pies of them every day, and nothing could surpass the felicity of the whole family.

One morning the King had been out hunting, and happened to ride by the cottage of Patroclus with a train of his knights. Daphne was baking pies as usual, and the kitchen door and window were both open, for the room was so warm; so the delicious odor of the pies perfumed the whole air about the cottage.

"What is it smells so utterly lovely?" exclaimed the King, sniffing in a rapture.

He sent his page in to see.

"The housewife is baking Giant's head pies," said the page, returning.

"What?" thundered the King. "Bring out one to me!"

So the page brought out a pie to him, and after all

his knights had tasted to be sure it was not poison, and the King had watched them sharply for a few moments to be sure they were not killed, he tasted, too.

Then he beamed. It was a new sensation, and a new sensation is a great boon to a king.

"I never tasted anything so altogether superfine, so utterly magnificent in my life," cried the King. "Stewed peacocks' tongues from the Baltic are not to be compared with it! Call out the housewife immediately!"

So Daphne came out trembling, and Patroclus and Æneas also.

"What a charming lad!" exclaimed the King as his glance fell upon Æneas. "Now tell me about these wonderful pies, and I will reward you as becomes a monarch!"

Then Patroclus fell on his knees and related the whole history of the Giant's head pies from the beginning.

The King actually blushed. "And I forgot to knight you, oh, noble and brave man, and to make a lady of your admirable wife!"

Then the King leaned gracefully down from his saddle, and struck Patroclus with his jeweled sword and knighted him on the spot.

The whole family went to live at the royal palace. The roses in the royal gardens were uprooted, and Giant's heads (or pumpkins, as they came to be called) were sown in their stead; all the royal parks also were turned into pumpkin fields.

Patroclus was in constant attendance on the King, and used to stand all day in his antechamber. Daphne had a position of great responsibility, for she superintended the baking of the pumpkin pies, and Æneas finally married the Princess Ariadne Diana.

They were wedded in great state by fifty archbishops, and all the newspapers united in stating that they were the most charming and well-matched young couple that had ever been united in the kingdom.

The stone entrance of the Pumpkin Giant's Castle was securely fastened, and upon it was engraved an inscription composed by the first poet in the kingdom, for which the king made him laureate, and gave him the liberal pension of fifty pumpkin pies per year.

The following is the inscription in full:

> "Here dwelt the Pumpkin Giant once,
> He's dead, the nation doth rejoice,
> For, while he was alive, he lived
> By e——g dear, fat little boys."

The inscription is said to remain to this day. If you were to go there you would probably see it.

Goody O'Grumpity

Carol Ryrie Brink

When Goody O'Grumpity baked a cake
The tall reeds danced by the mournful lake,
The pigs came nuzzling out of their pens,
The dogs ran sniffing and so did the hens,
And the children flocked by dozens and tens.
They came from the north, the east, and the south,
With wishful eyes and watering mouth,
And stood in a crowd about Goody's door,
Their muddy feet on her sanded floor.
And what do you s'pose they came to do!
Why, to lick the dish when Goody was through!
And throughout the land went such a smell
Of citron and spice—no words can tell
How cinnamon bark and lemon rind,
And round, brown nutmegs grated fine
A wonderful haunting perfume wove,

Together with allspice, ginger, and clove,
When Goody but opened the door of her stove.
The children moved close in a narrowing ring,
They were hungry—as hungry as bears in the spring;
They said not a word, just breathed in the spice,
And at last when the cake was all golden and nice,
Goody took a great knife and cut each a slice.

A Quick-Running Squash

Alicia Aspinwall

Charles owned a garden. One Thanksgiving morning his father called him and pointing to four stakes driven in the ground, which certainly had not been there the night before, said:

"All the land within those four stakes is yours, your very own."

Charles was delighted, and thanking his father ran off to get his little cart, for he wished at once to build a stone wall about his property. He did not fear it would run away, but he knew that landowners always walled in their possessions.

"After the wall is built," said his father, "you may plant in your garden anything you like, and James will give you what you ask for."

In two days the wall was built, and a good one it was, too, being strong and even.

The next day James set out some plants for him and gave the boy some seeds which he planted himself, James telling him how to do it.

He then got his watering pot and gently sprinkled the newly planted ground with warm water. Running across the lawn, he looked down the road to see if his father had not yet come from the village.

His father was nowhere to be seen, but coming down the road was a most remarkable-looking man. He was tall and thin and had bright red hair which had evidently not been cut for a very long time. He wore a blue coat, green trousers, red hat, and on his hands, which were large, two very dirty, ragged, white kid gloves.

This wonderful man came up to Charles and asked for a drink of water, which he, being a polite boy, at once brought. The man thanked him, and then said:

"What have you been doing this Thanksgiving morning, little man?"

Charles told him about his new garden, and the man listened with much interest.

"Little boy," said he, "there is one seed that you have not got."

"And what is that?"

"The seed of the quick-running squash."

Charles's face fell.

"I don't believe James has that, and I don't know where to get one," he faltered.

"Now, as it happens," said the man, "I have one of those very seeds in my pocket. It is not, however, that of the common, every-day, quick-running squash. This one came from India, and is marvelous for its quick-running qualities.

"You have been kind to me, little boy, and I will give it to you." And with a peculiar smile, this strange man produced from his pocket, instead of the ordinary squash seed, an odd, round, red seed which he gave to Charles, who thanked him heartily, and who ran to plant it at once. Having done so, he went back to ask when the quick-running squash would begin to grow.

But the man had disappeared, and although Charles looked up and down the dusty road, he could see nothing of him.

As he stood there, he heard behind him a little rustling noise, and turning, saw coming toward him a green vine. He had, of course, seen vines before, but never, never had he seen such a queer one as this. It was running swiftly toward him, and on the very front was a round yellow ball about as big as an orange!

Charles, looking back to see where it came from, found that it started in the corner of his garden. And what had he planted in that corner? Why, to be sure, the seed of the quick-running squash which the strange man had just given him.

"Well, well, well," he shouted, in great excitement, "what an *awfully* quick-running squash it is. I suppose that little yellow thing in front is the squash itself. But indeed it must not run away from me, I must stop it," and he darted swiftly down the street after it.

But, alas, no boy could run as fast as that squash, and

Charles saw far ahead the bright yellow ball now grown to be about the size of an ordinary squash, running and capering merrily over stones big and little, never turning out for anything, but bobbing up and down, up and down, and waving its long green vine like a tail behind it. The boy ran swiftly on. "It shall *not* get away," he panted. "It belongs to me."

But that the squash did not seem to realize at all. He did not feel that he belonged to anybody, and he *did* feel that he was a quick-running squash, and so on he scampered.

Suddenly he came to a very large rock, and stopped for a moment to take breath, and in that moment Charles caught up with him and simply sat down on him.

"Now, squash," said he, slapping him on the side, "your journey is ended."

The words were scarcely spoken when he suddenly felt himself lifted up in the air, and bumpity, bump, over the stone flew the squash, carrying with him his very much astonished little master! The squash had been growing all the time, and was now about three times as big as an ordinary one.

Charles, who had a pony of his own, knew how to ride, but never had he ridden anything so extraordinary as this. On they flew, "roll, waddle, bump, *bump;* roll, waddle, *bang,*" the boy digging his knees hard into the sides of the squash to avoid being thrown. He had a dreadfully hard time. Mount the next quick-running squash you meet, and you will see for yourself how it is.

To Charles's great delight he now saw his father coming toward him, riding his big black horse Nero, who was very much frightened when he saw the boy on such a strange yellow steed. But Nero soon calmed down at his master's voice, and, turning, rode along beside the squash, although he had to go at full speed to do so. "Gallopty-gallop" went Nero and "bumpity-bump" went the squash. Papa lost his hat (Charles had parted with his long before).

"What are you doing, my son, and what, *what* is it you are riding?" asked his father.

"A quick-running squash, Papa," gasped Charles, who, although bruised and aching, refused to give up the squash, and was still pluckily keeping his seat. "Stop it, oh, do stop it, Papa."

His father knew that this could be no ordinary squash, and saw that it evidently did not intend to stop.

"I will try to *turn* it and make it go back," he said, so riding Nero nearer and nearer the squash, he forced it up against a stone wall. But, instead of going back, this extraordinary squash jumped with scarcely a moment's hesitation over the high wall, and went bobbing along into the rough field beyond. But alas, before them was a broad lake, and as he could not swim, back he was forced to turn.

Over the wall and back again over the same road and toward the garden whence he came, Charles still on his back and Charles's papa galloping at full speed behind.

The squash, however, must have had a good heart,

for when he reached the house again, he of his own accord turned in at the gate and ran up to the wall of Charles's garden. There he stopped, for he was now so big that he could not climb walls, and indeed had he been able to get in he would have filled the little garden to overflowing, for he was really enormous.

Charles's father had actually to get a ladder for the poor little fellow to climb down, and he was so tired that he had to be carried to the house. But the squash was tired, too, dreadfully tired. I suppose it is a very bad thing for a growing squash to take much exercise. This certainly was a growing squash, and there is also no doubt that he had taken a great deal of exercise that morning.

Be that as it may, when the family were at luncheon they were alarmed at hearing a violent explosion near the house. Rushing out to see what could have happened, they found that the marvelous quick-running squash had *burst!* It lay spread all over the lawn in a thousand pieces.

The family, and all the neighbors' families for miles around, had squash pie for a week.

A New Pioneer

Dorothy Canfield Fisher

※ ※

A new girl came into the Winthrop Avenue public school about the beginning of November, and this is how she looked to the other boys and girls in the seventh grade.

She couldn't understand English although she could read it enough to get her lessons. (This was a small public school in a small inland American town where they seldom saw any foreigners, and people who couldn't speak English seemed outlandish.) She wore the queerest-looking clothes you ever saw and clumping shoes and great thick woolen stockings. (All the children in that town, as in most American towns, dressed exactly like everybody else, because their mothers mostly bought their clothes at Benning and Davis' department store on Main Street.)

Her hair wasn't bobbed and curled, neither a long

nor short bob; it looked as though her folks hadn't ever
had sense enough to bob it. It was done up in two funny-
looking pigtails. She had a queer expression on her face,
like nothing anybody had ever seen—kind of a smile and
yet kind of offish. She couldn't see the point of wise-
cracks, but she laughed over things that weren't funny
a bit, like the way a cheerleader waves his arms.

She got her lessons *terribly* well (the others thought
somebody at home must help her more than the teachers
like), and she was the dumbest thing about games—didn't
even know how to play duck on a rock or run sheep run.
And, queerest of all, she wore *aprons!* Can you beat
it!

That's how she looked to the school. This is how the
school looked to her. They had come a long way, she
and her grandfather, from the town in Austria where he
had a shop in which he repaired watches and clocks and
sold trinkets the peasant boys bought for their sweet-
hearts.

Men in uniforms and big boots had come suddenly
one day—it was in vacation, and Magda was there—and
had smashed in the windows of the shop and the show-
case with the pretty things in it and had thrown all the
furniture from their home back of the shop out into
the street and made a bonfire of it.

Magda had been hiding in a corner and saw this; and
now, after she had gone to sleep, she sometimes saw it
again and woke up with a scream, but Grandfather always came quickly to say smilingly, "All right, Magda

child. We're safe in America with Uncle Harry. Go to sleep again."

He had said she must not tell anybody about that day. "We can do something better in the New World than sow more hate," he said seriously. She was to forget about it if she could, and about the long journey afterward, when they were so frightened and had so little to eat; and, worst of all, when the man in the uniform in New York thought for a minute that something was wrong with their precious papers and they might have to go back.

She tried not to think of it, but it was in the back of her mind as she went to school every day, like the black cloth the jewelers put down on their counters to make their pretty gold and silver things shine more. The American school (really a rather ugly old brick building) was for Magda made of gold and silver, shining bright against what she tried to forget.

How kind the teachers were! Why, they *smiled* at the children. And how free and safe the children acted! Magda simply loved the sound of their chatter on the playground, loud and gay and not afraid even when the teacher stepped out for something. She did wish she could understand what they were saying.

She had studied English in her Austrian school, but this swift, birdlike twittering didn't sound a bit like the printed words on the page. Still, as the days went by she began to catch a word here and there, short ones like "down" and "run" and "back." And she soon found out what *hurrah!* means, for the Winthrop Avenue school made a specialty of mass cheering, and every grade had a cheerleader, even the first graders.

Magda thought nearly everything in America was as odd and funny as it was nice. But the cheerleaders were the funniest, with their bendings to one side and the other and then jumping up straight in the air till both feet were off the ground. But she loved to yell, "Hurrah!" too, although she couldn't understand what they were cheering about.

It seemed to her that the English language was like a thick, heavy curtain hanging down between her and her new schoolmates. At first she couldn't see a thing through it. But little by little it began to have thinner spots in it. She could catch a glimpse here and there of what they were saying when they sometimes stood in a group, looking at her and talking among themselves. How splendid it would be, she thought, to have the curtain down altogether so she could really understand what they were saying!

This is what they were saying—at least the six or seven girls who tagged after Betty Woodworth. Most of the seventh graders were too busy studying and racing around at recess time to pay much attention to the queer new girl. But some did. They used to say, "My goodness, look at that dress! It looks like her grandmother's—if she's got one."

"Of all the dumb clucks. She doesn't even know enough to play squat tag. My goodness, the first graders can play *tag*."

"My father told my mother this morning that he

didn't know why *our* country should take in all the disagreeable folks that other countries can't stand any
more."

"She's Jewish. She must be. Everybody that comes from
Europe now is Jewish. We don't want our town all filled
up with Jews!"

"My uncle Peter saw where it said in the paper we
ought to keep them out. We haven't got enough for ourselves as it is."

Magda could just catch a word or two, "country" and
"enough" and "uncle." But it wouldn't be long now,
she thought happily, till she could understand everything they said and really belong to seventh grade.

About two weeks after Magda came to school Thanksgiving Day was due. She had never heard of Thanksgiving Day, but since the story was all written out in her
history book she soon found out what it meant. She
thought it was perfectly lovely!

She read the story of the Pilgrim Fathers and their
long, hard trip across the ocean (she knew something
about that trip), and their terrible first winter, and the
kind Indian whose language they couldn't understand,
who taught them how to cultivate the fields, and then
—oh, it was poetry, just *poetry*, the setting aside of a day
forever and forever, every year, to be thankful that they
could stay in America!

How could people (as some of the people who wrote
the German textbooks did) say that Americans didn't
care about anything but making money? Why, here,

more than three hundred years after that day, this whole school and every other school, everywhere all over the country, were turning themselves upside down to celebrate with joy their great-grandfathers' having been brave enough to come to America and to stay here, even though it was hard, instead of staying in Europe, where they had been so badly treated. (Magda knew something about that, too.)

Everybody in school was to do something for the celebration. The first graders had funny little Indian clothes, and they were going to pretend to show the second graders (in Puritan costumes) how to plant corn. Magda thought they were delightful, those darling little things, being taught already to be thankful that they could go on living in America.

Some grades had songs; others were going to act in short plays. The children in Magda's own seventh grade, that she loved so, were going to speak pieces and sing. She had an idea all her own, and because she couldn't be sure of saying the right words in English she wrote a note to the teacher about it.

She would like to write a thankful prayer (she could write English pretty well now) and learn it by heart and say it, as her part of the celebration. The teacher, who was terrifically busy with a bunch of boys who were to build a small "pretend" log cabin on the stage, nodded that it would be all right. So Magda went away happily to write it and learn it by heart.

"Kind of nervy, if you ask me, of that little Jew girl to horn in on *our* celebration," said Betty.

"Who asked her to come to America, anyhow?" said another.

"I thought Thanksgiving was for *Americans!*" said another.

Magda, listening hard, caught the word "Americans," and her face lighted up. It wouldn't be long now, she thought, before she could understand them.

No, no, they weren't specially bad children, no more than you or I—they had heard older people talking like that—and they gabbled along, thoughtlessly, the way we are all apt to repeat what we hear, without considering whether it is right or not.

On Thanksgiving Day a lot of those grownups whose talk Betty and her gang had been repeating had come, as they always did, to the "exercises." They sat in rows in the assembly room, listening to the singing and acting of the children and saying, "the first graders are too darling," and "how time flies," and "can you believe it that Betty is up to my shoulder now? Seems like last week she was in the kindergarten."

The tall principal stood at one side of the platform and read off the different numbers from a list. By and by he said, "We shall now hear a prayer written by Magda Bensheim and spoken by her. Magda has been in this country only five weeks and in our school only three."

Magda came out to the middle of the platform, a bright, striped apron over her thick woolen dress, her braids tied with red ribbons. Her heart was beating fast. Her face was shining and solemn.

She put her hands together and lifted them up over her head and said to God, "Oh, thank you, thank you, dear God, for letting me come to America and nowhere else, when Grandfather and I were driven from our home. I learn out of my history book that Americans all came to this country just how Grandfather and I come, because Europe treat them wrong and bad. Every year they gather like this—to remember their brave grandfathers who come here so long ago and stay on, although they had such hard times.

"American hearts are so faithful and true that they forget never how they were all refugees, too, and must thankful be that from refugees they come to be American citizens. So thanks to you, dear, dear God, for letting Grandfather and me come to live in a country where they have this beautiful once-a-year Thanksgiving, for having come afraid from Europe to be here free and safe. I, too, feel the same beautiful thank-you-God that all we Americans say here today."

Magda did not know what is usually said in English at the end of a prayer so did not say anything when she finished, just walked away back where the other girls of her class were. But the principal said it for her—after he had given his nose a good blow and wiped his eyes. He looked out over the people in the audience and said in a loud, strong voice, "Amen! I say Amen, and so does everybody here, I know."

And then—it was sort of queer to applaud a prayer—they all began to clap their hands loudly.

Back in the seventh-grade room the teacher was saying, "Well, children, that's all. See you next Monday. Don't eat too much turkey." But Betty jumped up and said, "Wait a minute, Miss Turner. Wait a minute, kids. I want to lead a cheer. All ready?

"Three cheers for Magda!

"Hip! Hip!" She leaned 'way over to one side and touched the floor, and they all shouted, "Hurrah!"

She bent back to the other side. "Hurrah!" they shouted.

She jumped straight up till both feet were off the ground and clapped her hands over her head, and "Hurrah!" they all shouted.

The wonderful moment had come. The curtain that had shut Magda off from her schoolmates had gone. "Oh! Ach!" she cried, her eyes wide. "Why, I understood every word. Yes, now I can understand American!"

Old Tom's Thanksgiving Dinner

William Thomas Whitlock

Old Tom and I were prospecting along the eastern slopes of the Maricopa Range. I had furnished the grubstake and had gone along more for recuperation and experience than in hope of making a lucky strike.

Early one morning on our third day out from Barstown a shiftless, half-grown waif named Hank, whom I had at times befriended, stalked into camp and demanded something to eat. In some manner he had learned of our expedition and then had stealthily followed our trail across the desert until he was sure that we would not send him back to the settlements. "Ain't had nothin' but cactus pears and some berries since I left Barstown," he said, grinning impudently.

The presence of the boy enraged old Tom. "We've only brought grub enough fer two," he said. "With another mouth to feed we'll have to cut short our trip."

He turned to me. "Give him a good square meal and provisions for three days and tell him to vamoose back to where he came from."

To my astonishment Hank's bold eyes suddenly filled with tears. "Ain't got no place nor nobody to go to," he said and gulped. "And I want to be with him." He nodded toward me.

His attitude touched me, for all that I had ever given him were some of my old clothing, a few coins, and a meal now and then. "Oh, all right," I said hastily. "But you must do your share of the work about the camp to pay for your keep."

Hank nodded his head and then began ravenously to eat the food that old Tom had grudgingly placed before him.

Although Hank naturally was lazy, he faithfully performed the tasks that we assigned to him. But his appetite was enormous, and at meals old Tom would regard him with dismay.

"Every meal that young one devours shortens our prospectin' tour a whole day," he grumbled. "Oh, yes, I know we're doin' very well with the game we manage to kill, but we're up here to look fer minerals, not to be hunting grouse and rabbits."

By the first of October we had traveled for weeks without discovering any outcroppings of "minerals." Old Tom worked diligently over the plateaus and gulches of the foothills and often would return to camp, weary and dejected; but the next morning he would always rise with renewed vigor and hope. "I shore do want to find somethin' this trip," he declared. "I'm gettin' too old to be rangin' over these hills much longer."

A fortnight later we crossed the foothills and arrived at the rugged inclines of the Maricopas. Hank and I were as brown as Indians; our muscles were like steel, and both of us were enjoying the long tramps during the day, the hearty meals in camp, and the cool, sleep-inducing breezes of the elevations.

But the old prospector was looking haggard and worn over his failure to discover traces of minerals. "Do you happen to know what day of the month this is?" he asked one night.

"Must be the twenty-sixth of October," I replied.

"Humph. Four weeks to Thanksgivin'."

"Why, I had almost forgotten. What do you know about Thanksgiving?" I inquired, laughing.

"Warn't I born and raised in old Vermont? Reckon a feller ever fergits them feasts of turkey and stuffin', pumpkin pies an' mincemeat? And I ain't never failed to celebrate the day with some sort of extra feed. 'Bout time to knock off work and hit the trail fer the cabin," he added musingly.

"The cabin?" I asked in wonder.

But he had lapsed into one of his long, tight-lipped silences. He did not mention the subject again for several days. Then one night he ordered Hank to round up the pack burros early the next morning and to strike the tent while breakfast was preparing. He routed me from my blankets before daybreak, and soon after the sun came peeping up over the distant peaks we were on the march.

For ten days we traveled to the north and west. The trail ascended through the chaparral thickets and then, crossing the stunted cedar belt, finally wound along near the crest of an apparently endless spiny ridge. Old Tom seemed to have forgotten his eagerness to discover minerals. He made frequent halts to hunt for game, and he continued to grumble over the amount of food that Hank ate.

The old prospector was an excellent cook, and he refused to allow either Hank or me to aid in preparing the meals.

"You'd waste more than you'd cook," he declared. "And I never allow nobody to mess round my grub box anyway."

Hank's task was to rustle firewood, build the cook pit, and keep the blaze going beneath the pans and kettles. As he squatted near the fire he would observe closely each ingredient that the cook used and also the way he prepared the food. Indeed, his manner was so eager and inquisitive that the old man frequently was irritated.

"Go 'long away from here," old Tom said to him one night. "Can't you wait till I get things ready to eat, you hungry coyote cub!"

Hank retreated, somewhat abashed; but I noticed with amusement that he continued to watch old Tom's preparations as if the mere sight of food had made him ravenous.

Late in the afternoon of a hard day's march old Tom

paused on a little stony shelf and waited until Hank and I had brought up the pack animals.

"That's the cabin," he announced, pointing to a wider ledge a short distance farther up the mountains. "The only home I own in the world. Built that shack ten years ago—hauled the logs from the cedar strip on burros' backs and laid the stonework myself. Every year I come up here for my Thanksgivin' feast. If I've had good luck an' plenty of provisions, I sometimes stay till spring."

Half an hour later we had scrambled up to the stony bench and were gazing about us. Away in the distance to the south and east, spread out fanwise and glistening in the last rays of the sinking sun, lay the desert. To the north rose a chain of snow-capped peaks. To the south and west the bare, serrated ridge of the Maricopas extended for miles. The cabin, a rude building with a huge fireplace, sat near the center of the bench. In the rear a jumble of brownish boulders formed an irregular bald knob. It would be hard to imagine a more isolated, lonely spot.

A few yards from the front door a precipitous canyon dropped to a mountain stream, and on the opposite side the wall rose to another bench. Although the stream was only a tiny trickle among the rocks, I knew from the marks on the walls of the canyon that more than once terrific floods that cloudbursts or the sudden melting of the snow fields had caused had poured through the gorge.

On entering the cabin, old Tom began immediately

to rummage among some shelves in one corner of the room. "Guess we've got aplenty with what's here," he said at last. "I left these things last year, sealed up tight in cans so the pack rats couldn't get to 'em. I've brought cranberry jell and canned pumpkin, and I managed to save a few potatoes from Hank. Now all we need is a turkey."

"A turkey!" I exclaimed in derision. "I guess they're not very plentiful around here."

"I have shot 'em wild down in the cedar groves. That's one reason I built my cabin here. Some years I fail to discover 'em and have to go without; but Thanksgivin' is two weeks off, and now I intend to put in every day until I find one or know they ain't to be found."

For a week old Tom searched the cedar strips without bringing home even a partridge. I took the second rifle and wandered over the ledges, but I was no more fortunate than he.

One night he returned home with an especially worried and dejected air. "Nary a sight nor sign of a turkey, nor a grouse nor a quail neither," he said. "And we're going to have company for Thanksgivin', too."

"Company!" I cried.

"Thar's a little minin' settlement about ten miles to the southwest," he explained. "I tramped all the way down thar and back in hopes they might have shipped in a bird or two. But they didn't have no meat in the whole village but salt pork. When I told why I wanted a turkey two or three of the mine bosses hinted they'd like to bring their wives and come up to the cabin Thanksgivin' Day just to break the monotony of existence in a minin' camp."

"How about provisions? We shan't have enough left to continue prospecting," I protested.

"Oh, they'll bring plenty of canned stuff, and dishes, too. But we've just got to have a turkey or fresh meat of some sort."

"If we had another gun, I might go out and hunt, too," Hank suggested timidly.

"Huh! You wouldn't find nothin', and you'd come back with an appetite like a bear."

On the following morning, however, Hank pleaded so earnestly that I allowed him to take my rifle and depart while I remained at the cabin. He returned at nightfall, empty-handed; so did old Tom.

"Reckon it must be the weather that makes birds so scarce in these parts," said the prospector. "Never saw it so warm this time of year. When grouse and quail get on their winter coat o' feathers they can't endure much heat.

"Day after tomorrow is Thanksgivin'," he continued moodily. "I'd ought to stay home and bake my pumpkin pies, but I'm going to cross the canyon, climb up to the edge of the snow fields and see if the grouse and quail ain't migrated to a colder climate. If I don't find none today, I reckon we'll have to make out on canned salmon instead of a big fat gobbler."

Contrary to his custom, old Tom failed to return at

sunset. Hank and I sat up until midnight waiting for him. The boy pleaded insistently to be allowed to prepare supper. He said that he was starving; he knew I must be hungry and he was sure that the old man would not scold much if he found a hot meal all ready for him after climbing over the snow fields.

Out of patience at last, I prepared a cold lunch, and then, somewhat worried over the absence of the aged prospector, we went to bed.

When I awoke the next morning Hank had disappeared, and my rifle was missing from the rack on the wall. I spent a long, lonesome day at the cabin. The weather was uncomfortably warm; the burning sun glared upon the stony slope and ridges. The afternoon wore on, but neither of my companions put in an appearance. When the mountain twilight had deepened into dusk I built a rousing fire in the dooryard. Toward morning I must have fallen asleep.

At daybreak a loud, rumbling roar that seemed to come from the canyon roused me. Creeping to the brink of the ledge, I peered down. The gorge was half filled with a torrent of swirling, muddy water! I was creeping cautiously back from the dizzying sight when a shout made me glance across the gulch.

Old Tom was standing on the opposite rim; in his hands were two small quail, which he was brandishing with an air of disgust. "No chance to git across," he shouted above the roar of the flood. "Mile wide down below—snow still meltin' up on the peaks—may last for days—" He paused and stared stupidly at something on my side of the canyon.

I turned to behold Hank stumbling up the trail to the cabin. In his arms he clasped what I first mistook for a bear cub; then I saw that it was a big black wild-turkey gobbler!

Hank staggered across the bench and dropped the bird at my feet. "Shot him over in cedar grove on west ridge," he panted. "Found a turkey roost about sunset. Been all night luggin' this big fellow over the hills and gulches. Where's old Tom?"

I nodded to the solitary figure on the opposite bench. The old prospector was striding back and forth and waving his arms wildly. "Bird like that—company for dinner—nobody to cook—"

Hank made a megaphone of his hands. "Don't worry about that," he shouted. "I'll cook the dinner."

The old man threw out his hands and sank upon a boulder in an attitude of despair.

"All I'll ask you to do is to dress that turkey," Hank said to me curtly. Then he strode into the cabin.

Our guests arrived on a relay of saddle ponies late in the forenoon. Mr. Fink, the owner of the mines, and three of his employees brought their wives. When I had explained what had happened the men turned their attention to the prospector, and the women hastened into the cabin to help Hank to prepare the meal.

But the boy rejected all offers of assistance. "I'm cookin' this dinner," he declared with the irritable manner of old Tom when anyone disturbed him in his culinary labors.

Hank did, however, allow us to arrange a table in the center of the room and to provide seats from boxes and kegs. Then he drove us from the house into the pleasant autumn sunshine.

Old Tom was wandering restlessly along the bench on the opposite wall of the canyon. He gave little heed to the jests and condolences that we shouted across to him; he seemed to be absorbed in examining the formation of the ledge.

"He is probably prospecting to keep his mind off the dinner," said Fink, laughing.

"It is simply too bad that there's no way to send him some of the food," said Mrs. Fink. "I shall not enjoy my dinner for thinking of that poor old man sitting over there hungry."

"He is getting ready to roast one of the quails," replied the mine owner. "And perhaps we can save something for him to eat after the flood goes down."

We thought that dinner never would be ready, and we discussed the advisability of overpowering the youthful cook and taking matters into our own hands.

About two o'clock Hank opened the door. "I've thought of something," he announced eagerly. "We can tie a string to a bullet and shoot it over to old Tom. Then we can hitch on a heavier string and then a rope until we have a cable across the cañon. I'll fill one of the pack canisters with grub, ring it on the rope, and let slide to the opposite rim—"

"Say, you let me attend to that," interrupted Adams, one of the miners. "I've seen that done before."

Old Tom ceased his restless "prospecting" to listen to our plan. "Don't reckon the dinner'll be fit to eat," he shouted. "But mebbe it'll be better than roasted quail 'thout salt."

Fortunately, there were several balls of twine in the cabin. Adams took the bullet and part of the charge from a rifle cartridge and replaced them with two or three solid wads. Then he nested the string carefully on the ground and, tying one end of it to a cleaning rod, slipped the rod into the barrel of the gun. The arrangement reminded me of a whaler's harpoon gun that I had once seen.

Shooting the string across the gorge was a simple affair, but getting a cable long enough to bridge the canyon was not so easy; we hunted up and spliced together every foot of lariat, hobble rope, and other rope around the cabin. Nor could we find an elevation high enough to allow the canister to slide by gravity to old Tom.

"Shoot another string across for a towline," said Hank, who was filling the canister with food.

We glanced at one another rather foolishly; the suggestion was so simple and obvious.

At last everything was ready. Old Tom wound his end of the line around a boulder, and we fastened our end to the logs of the cabin. Hank placed the canister in a canvas bag and attached a large harness ring to it so that it would slip along the rope. We hooked on the towline and signaled for Tom to haul away. Would the cable hold? Was the towline strong enough?

We held our breath as the harness ring slid over the spliced places in the rope. The canvas bag with its precious contents seemed to hover for hours above the roaring, hissing flood, but at last old Tom reached out a long arm and grasped it. We gave a hearty cheer and then rushed into the cabin for our own feast.

Well, that was the best dinner I ever ate. The turkey was roasted to a turn, and there were mashed potatoes and gravy, oyster dressing, fried corn, cranberry jelly, and pumpkin pies. Hank had even baked a batch of hot biscuits in a camp skillet.

"Where in the world did you learn to cook?" I asked him.

"From watching old Tom about the campfire," he replied. "I like good things to eat, and I've always wanted to know how to cook. So I took lessons from one of the finest cooks in the land."

"You never saw him roast a turkey or bake pumpkin pies!"

"No, but we've both heard him dozens of times tell how he did it," replied Hank, laughing.

When we could eat no more we sauntered out into the yard to hear what old Tom thought of the dinner. The prospector had finished his meal and once more was striding thoughtfully back and forth along the ledge. To our astonishment he had driven three stakes at regular intervals into the crevices of the rock. He glanced up and beheld us assembled on the opposite bank.

"Struck it at last!" he shouted above the rumble of the flood. "Outcroppin's of the richest silver veins in the whole country! Right here across from my cabin all these years—while I was searchin' everywhere!"

"Stake out claims for the rest of us, Tom," the miners yelled excitedly.

Old Tom pointed impressively in turn to each of the stakes. "One fer me, one fer my partner, and one fer Hank! Boy who can cook a meal like that! Almost as good as I could do myself!"

The Thanksgiving Goose
Elizabeth Hough Sechrist

🍁 🍁

"Aunt Cora has always preferred goose to turkey," said Grandma as she helped herself to more applesauce.

The two little boys looked at her with alarm in their faces. It quickly changed to dismay when Grandpa said, "That reminds me, I'm going to kill that sassy Chinese gander for Thanksgiving this year. Tomorrow, in fact."

"Not Francis?" Lewis and Jeddie exclaimed together.

"Of course we'll have turkey besides," Mother said, trying not to notice the look on the boys' faces.

They were eating supper in the big farm kitchen. There were Grandfather, Grandmother, Father, Mother, the two boys, and Cherry, their little sister. It was only two days until Thanksgiving and the family had been discussing plans for the holiday. Aunt Cora and Uncle Tom were coming to spend the day with them.

"Grandpa, you just mustn't kill Francis!" Lewis said, his voice a wail.

Grandma snorted. "Francis! What a ridiculous name for a goose!"

"I love Francis," said Jeddie. "He eats corn right out of my hand, nice as anything!"

"I love Francis, too!" said Cherry, pounding her spoon on the table for emphasis.

"He's a consarned bossy pest, that's what he is," said Grandpa. "Why, only today he was fighting again. He's always picking on the younger geese. He's a big bully."

"But he doesn't mean any harm, Grandpa," said Lewis. "Daddy says he's cross because he lost his mate."

Jeddie appealed to his father. "Daddy, don't you let Grandpa kill Francis. He eats corn right out of my hand. And he's too tough to eat. Isn't he too tough, Daddy? Isn't he?"

But Father wasn't much comfort. "He's your grandfather's goose, Jeddie. You mustn't argue with Grandpa."

"There's no argument," Grandpa said emphatically. "It's the chopping block for Mr. Gander, and the other fowls will be better off without him."

At this Jeddie began to cry. He ran around the table to his mother and hid his head in her lap. Cherry set up a lusty howl in sympathy, and to add to the din the parrot from her cage began squawking in her shrill voice at the top of her lungs.

"Consarn it! I'm going out to do the milking." And Grandpa left the table, grabbed up his lantern, and disappeared out the back door.

Mother tried to console Jeddie. Grandmother stuffed a cookie into Cherry's mouth to distract her. Father jumped up and threw a cover over Polly's cage to stop her squawking.

Meanwhile Lewis was looking down at his plate dismally, thinking of Francis' awful fate. A tear rolled down his cheek and dropped into his dish of applesauce.

"Now, see here, you boys," said Father sternly. "Your grandfather is tired of catering to that infernal goose. Francis *is* a bully. I heartily agree with Grandpa that the very best place to put that fat, meddlesome bird is in the oven and on the Thanksgiving table."

Jeddie raised a tearful face. "But we l-love Francis."

"I'm sorry about that, Jeddie. I honestly am. You'll just have to realize that when you live on a farm there are bound to be some—er—some sad partings in store for you if you make friends with the animals."

Lewis thought for a moment. "You couldn't kill Jocko, Daddy, and *he's* a farm animal."

"Lewis, we don't eat donkeys. We do eat geese." He rose from the table. "Now, let's not talk about it any more."

When Father had gone outdoors to help Grandfather, the three children gathered around Mother. Grandmother started clearing away the dishes.

"Will Grandpa really do it, Mother?" asked Jeddie mournfully.

"I'm afraid so, Jeddie."

Lewis said fiercely, "All because of Aunt Cora! I *hate* Aunt Cora!" With that he rushed from the room and ran upstairs.

He was soon joined by Jeddie, who told him that

Mother said he must come downstairs and apologize for saying such a dreadful thing about Aunt Cora.

"Well, okay," said Lewis in a resigned voice. "I know I shouldn't have said it, but—say, Jeddie, can't you think of some way we can save Francis?"

"No, I wish I could. Why don't *you* think of something, Lewis?"

"Well, I have thought of one way we might save him. We might hide Francis so Grandpa couldn't find him. But that wouldn't do."

"Why not?" Jeddie wanted to know.

"It wouldn't be honest, and Grandpa would get awful mad if he couldn't find him."

"Oh, gosh! Then what are we going to do?"

Lewis shook his head solemnly. "I don't know, Jeddie. The worst of it is, we haven't much time. He'll kill Francis tomorrow because the next day is Thanksgiving."

While the boys were upstairs in their room talking, Mother and Grandmother were busy in the kitchen starting their preparations for the Thanksgiving Day feast. But Mother found time to cook up a batch of molasses candy for the children. She went to the foot of the stairs and called the boys.

"Lewis, if you and Jeddie would come down and shell the peanuts it would help me with this molasses candy I'm making."

It didn't take long for the boys to put in an appearance, and Cherry was there already, running from one cooking pot to another begging for tastes. Lewis went and stood in front of his grandmother.

"I'm sorry I said that about Aunt Cora."

"Your aunt Cora is very fond of you, Lewis," said Grandma.

"I know. I don't really hate her. I was mad!"

"Yes, I know," said Grandmother. "And we're sorry the goose has got to be killed. But I dare say that when you've tasted that delicious goose all brown and—"

Jeddie interrupted, stamping his foot angrily. "Grandma! Don't you say that! We won't eat a bite of Francis!"

"Come, boys, get busy with the peanuts," Mother said. She put a large bowl of peanuts on the table and spread out a newspaper for the shells. "My, these look good. Here, Cherry, you climb up on this chair and you can help, too."

So peace was restored, and for a while the only sounds in the room were the cracking of peanuts and the bubbling of things in the kettles on the stove. But Lewis's next remark to his mother showed where his thoughts had been all the while.

"Mother, I've thought of something. Why couldn't Grandpa sell Francis to someone who wants a good lively gander? Then we could buy a goose at the market for Thanksgiving."

His mother had been stirring the molasses mixture. She stopped her stirring and dropped a spoonful of the hot syrup into a saucer of cold water.

"It's done," she announced.

Grandma quickly buttered a large platter and the boys dumped a bowl of shelled peanuts onto the platter. The odor of the candy as Mother poured it over the peanuts was almost enough to distract Lewis from his question. But not quite.

"Couldn't we, Mother? Couldn't we do that?"

His mother looked at him sadly and shook her head. "I do declare, Lewis, you have a one-track mind. Son, I do wish you could stop thinking of that goose. And you know that Daddy asked us not to talk about it."

So for the remainder of the evening nobody talked about Francis. As to what they thought, that was a different matter. And the thoughts of the two boys were concentrated on the hope that some strange and wonderful miracle would happen to save their friend from the chopping block.

When the children woke up next morning they were delighted to see a light covering of snow on the ground. But their pleasure was soon dampened when they remembered that this was to be the fateful day for their pet gander.

While they were eating breakfast Grandfather came into the kitchen.

"If you boys will be ready in twenty minutes I'll take you into town with me. The belt on the saw motor is broken, and Jim Burns is here to help your father to work on the new stalls in the barn."

The boys were delighted. "We're ready now, Grandpa!" said Lewis, and Jeddie jumped up from the table with his toast in his hand, exclaiming, "Oh, boy! We're going to town with Grandpa."

It was always a treat to go into town. Grandpa never failed to stop at the drugstore, giving each of the boys a dime to spend any way they wished. Usually they bought ice-cream cones. But sometimes Jeddie bought a new ball or a toy. Lewis's sweet tooth always won out in his decision, and even now, as he and Jeddie ran out to the barnyard to wait for Grandpa to get out the old truck, he could taste the sweets he planned to buy.

Almost without thinking the boys wandered over to the small pond that lay east of the barn. Most of the ducks and geese were standing restlessly in groups near the water, waiting for their breakfast of corn.

"There's Francis!" shouted Jeddie, and he and Lewis crossed the planks which formed a boardwalk over the marshy ground. It was from this point that the ducks and geese were always fed. When the boys began walking toward them, the ducks set up a loud clatter, closing in and looking for corn. Francis, who had been busily pecking in the mud looking for bugs, came hurriedly, half-running, half-flying toward them. The sun gleamed on his white feathers. He stretched his long neck out to its full length, then drew it in; stretched it out, and drew it in with excitement.

Lewis put one hand in the pocket of his blue jeans.

"Shucks, Francis, I've only got one or two kernels of corn in my pocket."

"I've got some, Francis," said Jeddie. "Here, boy!"

Jeddie always had corn in his pockets. He held out his hand and Francis, unafraid, came close to the boy and, with staccato movements of his sharp bill, found the yellow kernels. Lewis stood by, looking on sadly, his eyes misted with tears.

"Gosh," was all he could say.

The two stood motionless while Francis made a business of probing into their pockets for more corn.

Just then Mother and Cherry appeared. Mother had an old bucket filled with corn. Cherry carried her own small pail, filled to the brim. Soon the mallards and 'scovies were crowding about them, pushing one another in their haste to eat the corn that was tossed to them. But the geese were always more reticent. With quiet dignity they waited until their share was thrown in their direction. That is, all but Francis. He nearly crawled into Jeddie's arms trying to get the corn away from him.

"Isn't he a mess?" laughed Jeddie, pushing the gander away from him, then holding out his palm so Francis could eat from it. "Look, Mother, just see how he eats from my hand, like it was a plate!"

Mother nodded and smiled but said nothing, perhaps because she found a lump in her throat. And just then the pickup truck came noisily around the side of the barn and Grandfather called to the boys. They both threw generous handfuls of corn in Francis' direction and ran toward the car.

"At least he's safe until we get back," Lewis whispered.

Mother and Cherry waved after the car until it disappeared up the road.

"Cherry, why don't you finish feeding the ducks and geese for me?" her mother said. "I'll go up and feed the chickens."

Cherry agreed, and she began by throwing fistfuls of corn in every direction. "It goes down into the snow, Mother," she complained.

"Go and stand under the tree, honey, where the ground is drier," Mother suggested. Under the big walnut tree in the field, a little beyond the pond, there was a place bare of snow. So, as her mother had suggested, Cherry proceeded to feed the big birds from there. Her mother went on to the chicken house to finish her feeding chores.

Francis, as usual, pushed the other ducks and geese rudely out of his way while he ate the largest share.

"You piggy, you!" Cherry scolded. Then she stood for a moment contemplating him. In a different and softer tone she said, "Poor Francis. Poor, poor Francis!"

For another minute she watched him eat. It would have been hard to guess what was going on in the little girl's mind. She looked all about her and suddenly started to walk away from the tree. Dropping corn and calling to Francis, she kept on until she had come to the fence at the edge of the field. Here she found what she had evidently been looking for.

Close to the fence there was an old wooden crate lying on its side. The hinged top was missing and some of the slats were broken. It had probably been discarded and forgotten by everyone but Cherry. Cherry remembered it because she had used it often to stand on when she wanted to climb the fence. Now she could think of another use for it.

The space beside the crate seemed to Cherry a good place to put all the rest of her corn. She emptied it in a heap, and Francis rushed greedily upon the kernels. Cherry was watching. There was the crate, and there was Francis, so close to it. She moved quietly until she stood directly behind the wooden box. A little shove; it moved. Francis was very busy eating and noticed nothing. Another little shove. Then a big push, and the crate went over.

It was nearly two hours later that Grandfather and the boys returned. Grandfather went to the barn while Lewis and Jeddie ran immediately to find Mother.

"Mother, come see what we bought!" Lewis shouted excitedly. But he need not have shouted for Mother was right there in the kitchen with Grandmother, baking pies for the morrow. Cherry, as usual, was at their heels.

Lewis opened a paper bag and brought out two small candles which he placed on the table. They were in the form of Pilgrims, one a Pilgrim man holding a musket, the other a little Pilgrim lady in a gray-and-white dress and bonnet, her hands clasped piously before her. They all exclaimed with pleasure, while the boys stood by beaming with satisfaction at their purchase.

"They're for you and Grandmother," Lewis said.

"Well, I never!" Grandma exclaimed with pleasure.

"They're just as cute as they can be," Mother said,

picking up the candles to examine them more closely. "We'll put them on the Thanksgiving table, won't we, Grandma?"

Grandma said yes, they certainly would. And she gave both boys a hug, and a special one for Lewis because she knew what a sacrifice it must have been for him to forego the usual sweets.

"Did you have a good time with Grandpa?" Mother asked as she went back to rolling pastry on a floured board.

"Oh, sure!" Jeddie answered promptly. "We stopped at the Wilsons' and Grandpa bought a great big live turkey gobbler for Thanksgiving dinner."

At the mention of the turkey a shadow crossed Lewis's face and he went over to the window and stood looking out. After a moment he turned and said crossly, "That turkey's big enough to feed an army! I don't see why we've got to have goose, too!"

Just at that moment the door opened and Grandpa entered the kitchen.

"Well, Jim Burns fixed the saw. He and the children's daddy have a good day's work ahead of them to finish before dark." He turned to Grandma. "Grandma, how about pouring me a nice hot cup of coffee, and then I'll go out and chop—" He checked himself, looking quickly at the boys. "We brought home a nice fat turkey," he continued. "You'd better put a big kettle of water on the stove." No one said a word. Grandpa now turned to Mother.

"Say, how about letting the boys shell those mixed

nuts we bought at the store for your nut cake? Cherry will help, too, won't you, baby?"

Mother said the boys could shell the nuts, and as soon as the pies were in the oven she would make the nut cake. She looked questioningly at Grandpa as she talked, and he nodded back at her. Mother and Grandma knew that Grandpa was going to take care of more than the turkey. And the boys knew it, too.

After Grandpa had drunk his coffee he went out. Lewis, from the window, saw him stop at the tool shed and emerge with the ax. He turned about, clenching his fists.

"I guess Grandpa thinks we're little kids not to know he's going to chop Francis' head off!" he exclaimed.

"Lewis," said his mother sternly, "you are the eldest and I think you should set a good example for the younger ones by accepting what has to be."

Lewis cast his eyes downward and made no answer. Jeddie looked from one to the other, then started to run for the back door. "I won't let him! I won't let him kill Francis!" he cried, and pulled open the door. But Mother called to him sharply, and bade him come back.

"Now I want you all to be sensible!" Then, her eyes falling on the little Pilgrim candles, she said, "Remember how the Pilgrims killed turkeys and other wild things for their Thanksgiving dinner? Grandma, suppose you tell the children the story of the first Thanksgiving, and we can look at the little Pilgrim candles and try to imagine just how it must have been."

Cherry seemed to be the only one interested in the

story Grandma began to tell, and she hung onto every word with great satisfaction. But Grandma hadn't got very far when she was interrupted by Grandpa, who came storming into the house looking very angry.

"Where's that infernal gander?" he shouted, addressing the two boys.

They looked at him in genuine surprise.

"Where did you hide him? Speak up now."

"We—we didn't hide him, Grandpa," Jeddie avowed.

"Is Francis gone?" Lewis asked hopefully.

"I don't know how far he's gone, but I'll warrant you boys do!" And Grandfather glared at them. Then he turned to Mother. "They're your young'uns. Tell them to go out there and find that goose so I can get this business over with and get back to my other work."

But Mother's face wore a puzzled frown as she said, "I don't understand, Papa. The boys couldn't have hidden Francis because he was out there with Cherry and me when the boys left with you. And they came into the house as soon as you returned. No, Grandpa, the boys haven't hidden the goose. He was out there with the others when Cherry finished feeding them."

" 'Deed he was, Grandpa!" piped up Cherry.

Grandpa scratched his head in a puzzled fashion. "I don't understand," he said. "That goose wouldn't have flown away because his wings are clipped. He just must be out there somewhere. Well, come on, boys. Help me to find him."

"I'll help, too," said Cherry, going for her coat. The

boys and Cherry ran outside with Grandpa. They looked everywhere, or so they thought. The boys even walked through the marshy ground surrounding the pond, looking through the high grass, and calling Francis' name. When they returned, Cherry was standing on the wooden boardwalk where she had been watching them. When the boys drew near she began to laugh.

"What are you laughing at, silly?" asked Lewis.

"Don't you wish you knew, don't you wish you knew?" she sang in her most provoking manner. But the boys paid no attention to her and presently she went back to the house to help Mother and Grandma with the pies and cakes.

By suppertime Grandpa was so annoyed and upset that he forbade anyone to mention the gander's name. The turkey had been plucked and dressed, and as soon as the supper dishes were done Mother sat down to make the stuffing. The boys had left to go on a private search of their own for their pet. Cherry was curled up on the settee, half-asleep.

"I declare, Mother," whispered Cherry's mother, "I just can't figure out what could have happened to Francis."

"Look," said Grandma softly. "Cherry is smiling in her sleep. I guess she's dreaming about Thanksgiving."

Everybody was up bright and early on Thanksgiving Day, for there were still many things to be done. The turkey was put into the oven at an early hour. By twelve o'clock the smells that filled the kitchen were almost too wonderful to be borne. The table was set with two extra places and the little Pilgrims were placed in the center, one on either side of a bowl of late yellow chrysanthemums.

At precisely twelve-thirty Uncle Tom's sedan drove into the yard. Everyone ran to the kitchen door to greet the guests. As they entered, Aunt Cora sniffed the air expressively.

"Mmm! I never smelled anything so good in all my life. I do believe it smells like goose."

Before anyone could reply to this remark Uncle Tom turned to Grandpa and said, "By the way, Father, what's going on up in the field?"

"Eh? Where?"

"Why, up along the fence, at the edge of the field. As we came down the road we could see the ducks raising a great clatter about something. They've all left the pond and are crowded together up there as though something had gotten after them. Maybe it's a fox."

The men and boys didn't lose any time getting out to the field to see what was the matter. Cherry, as soon as she could get into her coat, followed after them.

They could see as they came closer that the ducks, instead of being frightened, were assembled like an interested crowd watching a parade. Their eyes were centered on something that looked like a dancing box. Now there is nothing more curious than a duck, and as his curiosity mounts his excitement rises. They were grouped about an old crate, jostling and pushing one another to get a closer look. Grandpa and the others edged in closer, too, and then they saw that the crate was moving and pushing about as though possessed. There was only one conclusion to make.

"There's something inside that crate!" Father shouted. He waded through the ducks and gave the crate a push, and there before their astounded eyes was Francis!

"Francis!" shrieked Jeddie, running toward the gander.

But Francis was very angry. His feathers were ruffled and dirty. With an angry honk he half-flew, half-ran away from them as fast as he could go.

"Now how did that goose get under that box?" remarked Uncle Tom in wonderment.

"How long do you suppose he was under there?" asked Father.

"I think the boys can answer all those questions," Grandpa said in a stern voice.

"Lewis and Jeddie, did you hide Francis?"

The boys looked straight at their father. "Honest, we didn't," they said.

There was a tense silence for a moment and, by the expression on Grandpa's face, it seemed as though this Thanksgiving Day was doomed to be an unhappy one.

"I did it! I saved Francis. I love Francis."

They all turned to look at Cherry, and even as she spoke she ran over to the crate and showed them how she had pushed it over Francis to hide him from Grandpa.

"And I gave him lots and lots of corn so he wouldn't get hungry," she explained.

Well, even Grandpa had to laugh, finally. And when they went indoors they had to tell it to the others, and they all laughed, too.

"It's a wonder Francis didn't raise a fuss, being a prisoner all that time," Jeddie said.

"Well," Grandma laughed. "I think Francis was a stuffed goose—too full of corn to make a fuss!"

By the time they sat down to dinner everyone was in a happy mood.

"I believe I'm going to have a second helping of that turkey," Aunt Cora said as she held out her plate for Father to refill it. "I never realized it before, but I believe I like turkey every bit as well as goose."

Lewis nudged Jeddie, and they smiled secretly at each other as they thought of Francis.

When the Frost is on the Punkin

James Whitcomb Riley

When the frost is on the punkin and the fodder's in the
shock,
And you hear the kyouck and gobble of the struttin'
turkey-cock,
And the clackin' of the guineys, and the cluckin' of the
hens,
And the rooster's hallylooyer as he tiptoes on the fence;
Oh, it's then's the times a feller is a-feelin' at his best,
With the risin' sun to greet him from a night of peace-
ful rest,
As he leaves the house, bareheaded, and goes out to feed
the stock,
When the frost is on the punkin and the fodder's in the
shock.

They's something kind o' harty-like about the atmus-
   fere

When the heat of summer's over and the coolin' fall is
   here—

Of course we miss the flowers, and the blossoms on the
   trees,

And the mumble of the hummin'-birds and buzzin' of
   the bees;

But the air's so appetizin'; and the landscape through
   the haze

Of a crisp and sunny morning of the airly autumn
   days

Is a pictur' that no painter has the colorin' to mock—

When the frost is on the punkin and the fodder's in the
   shock.

The husky, rusty russel of the tossels of the corn,

And the raspin' of the tangled leaves, as golden as the
   morn;

The stubble in the furries—kind o' lonesome-like, but
   still

A-preachin' sermuns to us of the barns they growed to
   fill;

The strawstack in the medder, and the reaper in the
   shed;

The hosses in theyr stalls below—the clover overhead!—

Oh, it sets my hart a clickin' like the tickin' of a clock,

When the frost is on the punkin and the fodder's in the
   shock.

Then your apples all is gethered, and the ones a feller
    keeps
Is poured around the celler-floor in red and yeller heaps;
And your cider-makin' 's over, and your wimmern-folks
    is through
With their mince and apple-butter, and theyr souse and
    saussage, too!

I don't know how to tell it—but ef sich a thing could be
As the Angels wantin' boardin', and they'd call around
    on *me*—
I'd want to 'commodate 'em—all the whole-indurin'
    flock
When the frost is on the punkin and the fodder's in the
    shock!

Ezra's Thanksgivin' Out West

Eugene Field

Ezra had written a letter to the home folks, and in it he had complained that never before had he spent such a weary, lonesome day as this Thanksgiving Day had been.

Having finished this letter, he sat for a long time gazing idly into the open fire that snapped cinders all over the hearthstone and sent its red forks dancing up the chimney to join the winds that frolicked and gamboled across the Kansas prairies that raw November night.

It had rained hard all day, and was cold; and although the open fire made every honest effort to be cheerful, Ezra, as he sat in front of it in the wooden rocker and looked down into the glowing embers, experienced a dreadful feeling of loneliness and homesickness.

"I'm sick o' Kansas," said Ezra to himself. "Here I've been in this plaguey country for goin' on a year, and—

226

yes, I'm sick of it, powerful sick of it. What a miser'ble Thanksgivin' this has been! They don't know what Thanksgivin' is out this way. I wish I was back in ol' Mass'chusetts—that's the country for *me,* and they hev the kind o' Thanksgivin' I like!"

Musing in this strain, while the rain went patter-patter on the windowpanes, Ezra saw a strange sight in the fireplace—yes, right among the embers and the crackling flames Ezra saw a strange, beautiful picture unfold and spread itself out like a panorama.

"How very wonderful!" murmured the young man. Yet he did not take his eyes away, for the picture soothed him and he loved to look upon it.

"It is a pictur' of long ago," said Ezra softly. "I had like to forgot it, but now it comes back to me as nat'ral-like as an ol' friend. An' I seem to be a part of it, an' the feelin' of that time comes back with the pictur', too."

Ezra did not stir. His head rested upon his hand, and his eyes were fixed upon the shadows in the firelight.

"It is a pictur' of the ol' home," said Ezra to himself. "I am back there in Belchertown, with the Holyoke hills up north an' the Berkshire Mountains a-loomin' up gray an' misty-like in the western horizon.

"Seems as if it wuz early mornin'; everythin' is still, and it is so cold when we boys crawl out o' bed that, if it wuzn't Thanksgivin' mornin', we'd crawl back again an' wait for Mother to call us. But it *is* Thanksgivin' mornin', and we're goin' skatin' down on the pond.

"The squealin' o' the pigs has told us it is five o'clock,

and we must hurry; we're goin' to call by for the Dickerson boys an' Hiram Peabody, an' we've got to hyper! Brother Amos gets on about helf o' my clothes, and I get on 'bout half o' his, but it's all the same; they are stout, warm clo'es, and they're big enough to fit any of us boys—Mother looked out for that when she made 'em.

"When we go downstairs, we find the girls there, all bundled up nice an' warm—Mary an' Helen an' Cousin Irene. They're going with us, an' we all start out tiptoe and quiet-like so's not to wake up the ol' folks. The ground is frozen hard; we stub our toes on the frozen ruts in the road. When we come to the minister's house, Laura is standin' on the front stoop awaitin' for us.

"Laura is the minister's daughter. She's a friend o' Sister Helen's—pretty as a dagerr'otype, an' gentle-like and tender. Laura lets me carry her skates, an' I'm glad of it, although I have my hands full already with the lantern, the hockies, and the rest.

"Hiram Peabody keeps us waitin', for he has overslept himself, an' when he comes trottin' out at last the girls make fun of him—all except Sister Mary, an' she sort o' sticks up for Hiram, an' we're all so 'cute we kind o' calc'late we know the reason why.

"And now," said Ezra softly, "the pictur' changes: seems as if I could see the pond. The ice is like a black lookin' glass, and Hiram Peabody slips up the first thing, an' down he comes, lickety-split, an' we all laugh—except Sister Mary, an' *she* says it is very imp'lite to laugh at other folks' misfortunes.

"Ough! How cold it is, and how my fingers ache with the frost when I take off my mittens to strap on Laura's skates! But, oh, how my cheeks burn! And how careful I am not to hurt Laura, an' how I ask her if that's 'tight enough,' an' how she tells me 'jist a little tighter,' and how we two keep foolin' along till the others hev gone an' we are left alone!

"An' how quick I get my *own* skates strapped on—none o' your newfangled skates with springs an' plates an' clamps an' such, but honest, ol'-fashioned wooden ones with steel runners that curl up over my toes an' have a bright brass button on the end! How I strap 'em and lash 'em and buckle 'em on! An' Laura waits for me an' tells me to be sure to get 'em on tight enough—why, bless me! after I once got 'em strapped on, if them skates hed come off, the feet wud ha' come with 'em!

"An' now away we go—Laura and me. Around the bend—near the medder where Si Baker's dog killed a woodchuck last summer—we meet the rest. We forget all about the cold. We run races an' play snap the whip, an' cut all sorts o' didoes, an' we never mind the pick'rel weed that is froze in on the ice an' trips us up every time we cut the outside edge; an' then we boys jump over the air holes, an' the girls stan' by an' scream an' tell us they know we're agoin' to drownd ourselves.

"So the hours go, an' it is sunup at last, an' Sister Helen says we must be gettin' home. When we take our skates off, our feet feel as if they were wood. Laura has lost her tippet; I lend her mine, and she kind o' blushes. The old pond seems glad to have us go, and the fire hangbird's nest in the willer tree waves us good-by. Laura promises to come over to our house in the evenin', and so we break up.

"Seems now," continued Ezra musingly, "seems now as if I could see us all at breakfast. The race on the pond has made us hungry, and Mother says she never knew anybody else's boys that had such capac'ties as hers.

"It is the Yankee Thanksgivin' breakfast—sausages an' fried potatoes, an' buckwheat cakes, an' syrup—maple syrup, mind ye, for Father has his own sugar bush, and there was a big run o' sap last season. Mother says, 'Ezry an' Amos, won't you never get through eatin'? We want to clear off the table, fer there's pies to make, and nuts to crack, and laws sakes alive! The turkey's got to be stuffed yet!'

"Then how we all fly around! Mother sends Helen up into the attic to get a squash while Mary's makin' the piecrust. Amos an' I crack the walnuts—they call 'em hickory nuts out in this pesky country of sagebrush and pasture land. The walnuts are hard, and it's all we can do to crack 'em.

"Ev'ry once'n awhile one of 'em slips outer our fingers and goes dancin' over the floor or flies into the pan Helen is squeezin' pumpkin into through the col'nder. Helen says we're shif'less an' good for nothin' but frivolin'; but Mother tells us how to crack the walnuts so's not to let 'em fly all over the room, an' so's not to be all jammed to pieces like the walnuts was down at the party at the Peasleys' last winter.

"An' now here comes Tryphena Foster, with her

gingham gown an' muslin apron on; her folks have gone
up to Amherst for Thanksgivin', an' Tryphena has come
over to help our folks get dinner. She thinks a great deal
o' Mother, 'cause Mother teaches her Sunday-school class
an' says Tryphena oughter marry a missionary.

"There is bustle everywhere, the rattle uv pans an'
the clatter of dishes; an' the new kitchen stove begins to
warm up an' git red, till Helen loses her wits and is
flustered, an' sez she never could git the hang o' that
stove's dampers.

"An' now," murmured Ezra gently, as a tone of deeper
reverence crept into his voice, "I can see Father sittin'
all by himself in the parlor. Father's hair is very gray,
and there was wrinkles on his honest old face. He is
lookin' through the winder at the Holyoke hills over
yonder, and I can guess he's thinkin' of the time when
he wuz a boy like me an' Amos, an' uster climb over
them hills an' kill rattlesnakes an' hunt partridges.

"Or doesn't his eyes quite reach the Holyoke hills?
Do they fall kind o' lovingly but sadly on the little
buryin' ground jest beyond the village? Ah, Father
knows that spot, an' he loves it, too, for there are treasures there whose memory he wouldn't swap for all the
world could give.

"So, while there is a kind o' mist in Father's eyes, I
can see he is dreamin'-like of sweet an' tender things,
and a-communin' with memory—hearin' voices I never
heard, an' feelin' the tech of hands I never pressed; an'

seein' Father's peaceful face I find it hard to think of a Thanksgivin' sweeter than Father's is.

"The pictur' in the firelight changes now," said Ezra, "an' seems as if I wuz in the old frame meetin'house. The meetin'house is on the hill, and meetin' begins at half-pas' ten. Our pew is well up in front—seems as if I could see it now. It has a long red cushion on the seat, and in the hymn-book rack there is a Bible an' a couple of Psalmodies.

"We walk up the aisle slow, and Mother goes in first; then comes Mary, then me, then Helen, then Amos, and then Father. Father thinks it is jest as well to have one o' the girls set in between me an' Amos.

"The meetin'house is full, for everybody goes to meetin' Thanksgivin' Day. The minister reads the proclamation an' makes a prayer, an' then he gives out a psalm, an' we all stan' up an' turn 'round an' join the choir. Sam Merritt has come up from Palmer to spend Thanksgivin' with the ol' folks, an' he is singin' tenor today in his ol' place in the choir. Some folks say he sings wonderful well, but *I* don't like Sam's voice. Laura sings soprano in the choir, and Sam stands next to her an' holds the book.

"Seems as if I could hear the minister's voice, full of earnestness an' melody, comin' from way up in his little round pulpit. He is tellin' us why we should be thankful, an', as he quotes Scriptur' an' Dr. Watts, we boys wonder how anybody can remember so much of the Bible.

"Then I get nervous and worried. Seems to me the

minister was never comin' to lastly, and I find myself wonderin' whether Laura is listenin' to what the preachin' is about, or is writin' notes to Sam Merritt in the back of the tune book. I get thirsty, too, and I fidget about till Father looks at me, and Mother nudges Helen, and Helen passes it along to me with interest.

"An' then," continues Ezra in his revery, "when the last hymn is given out an' we stan' up agin an' join the choir, I am glad to see that Laura is singin' outer the book with Miss Hubbard, the alto. An' goin' out o' meetin' I kind of edge up to Laura and ask her if I kin have the pleasure of seein' her home.

"An' now we boys all go out on the Common to play ball. The Enfield boys have come over, and, as all the Hampshire County folks know, they are tough fellers to beat. Gorham Polly keeps tally, because he has got the newest jackknife—oh, how slick it whittles the old broom handle Gorham picked up in Packard's store an' brought along jest to keep tally on! It is a great game of ball; the bats are broad and light, and the ball is small and soft.

"But the Enfield boys beat us at last; leastwise they make 70 tallies to our 58, when Herman Fitts knocks the ball over into Aunt Dorcas Eastman's yard, and Aunt Dorcas comes out an' picks up the ball an' takes it into the house, an' we have to stop playin'. Then Phineas Owen allows he can flop any boy in Belchertown, an' Moses Baker takes him up, an' they wrassle like two tartars, till at last Moses tuckers Phineas out an' downs him as slick as a whistle.

"Then we all go home, for Thanksgivin' dinner is ready. Two long tables have been made into one, and one of the big tablecloths Gran'ma had when she set up housekeepin' is spread over 'em both. We all set round —Father, Mother, Aunt Lydia Holbrook, Uncle Jason, Mary, Helen, Tryphena Foster, Amos, and me. How big an' brown the turkey is, and how good it smells!

"There are bounteous dishes of mashed potatoes, turnip, an' squash, and the celery is very white and cold, the biscuits are light and hot, and the stewed cranberries are red as Laura's cheeks. Amos and I get the drumsticks; Mary wants the wishbone to put over the door for Hiram, but Helen gets it. Poor Mary, she always *did* have to give up to 'rushin' Helen,' as we call her.

"The pies—oh, what pies Mother makes; no dyspepsia in 'em, but good nature an' good health an' hospitality! Pumpkin pies, mince, an' apple, too, and then a big dish of pippins an' russets an' bellflowers, an', last of all, walnuts with cider from the Zebrina Dickerson farm!

"I tell ye, there's a Thanksgivin' dinner for ye! That's what we get in old Belchertown; an' that's the kind of livin' that makes the Yankees so all-fired good an' smart.

"But the best of all," said Ezra very softly to himself, "oh, yes, the best scene in all the pictur' is when evenin' comes, when all the lamps are lit in the parlor, when the neighbors come in, and when there is music and singin' an' games. An' it's this part o' the pictur' that makes me homesick now and fills my heart with a longin' I never had before; an' yet it sort o' mellows and comforts me, too.

"Miss Serena Cadwell, whose beau was killed in the war, plays on the melodeon, and we all sing—all of us: men, womenfolks, an' children. Sam Merritt is there, and he sings a tenor song about love. The women sort of whisper round that he's goin' to be married to a Palmer lady nex' spring, an' I think to myself I never heard better singin' than Sam's.

"Then we play games—proverbs, buzz, clap-in-clap-out, copenhagen, fox an' geese, button-button-who's-got-the-button, spin-the-platter, go-to-Jerusalem, my-ship's-come-in, and all the rest.

"The ol' folks play with the young folks just as nat'ral as can be; and we all laugh when Deacon Hosea Cowles hez to measure six yards of love ribbon with Miss Hepsey Newton, and cut each yard with a kiss, for the deacon hez been sort o' purrin' 'round Miss Hepsy for goin' on two years.

"Then, aft'r awhile, when Mary and Helen bring in the cookies, nut cakes, cider, an' apples, Mother says: 'I don't believe we're goin' to hev enough apples to go round; Ezry, I guess I'll have to get you to go down cellar for some more.' Then I says: 'All right, Mother, I'll go, providin' someone'll go along an' hold the candle.'

"An' when I say this I look right at Laura, an' she blushes. Then Helen, jest for meanness, says: 'Ezry, I s'pose you ain't willin' to have your fav'rite sister go down cellar with you and catch her death o' cold?'

But Mary, who hez been showin' Hiram Peabody the phot'graph album for more'n an hour, comes to the rescue an' makes Laura take the candle, and she shows Laura how to hold it so it won't go out.

"The cellar is warm an' dark. There are cobwebs all between the rafters an' everywhere else except on the shelves where Mother keeps the butter an' eggs an' other things that would freeze in the butt'ry upstairs. The apples are in bar'ls up against the wall, near the potater bin. How fresh an' sweet they smell!

"Laura thinks she sees a mouse, an' she trembles an' wants to jump up on the pork bar'l, but I tell her that there shan't no mouse hurt her while I'm around; and I mean it, too, for the sight of Laura a-tremblin' makes me as strong as one of Father's steers.

" 'What kind of apples do you like best, Ezry?' asks Laura, 'russets or greenin's or crow-eggs or bellflowers or Baldwins or pippins?'

" 'I like the Baldwins best,' says I, ' 'coz they got red cheeks just like yours!'

" 'Why, Ezry Thompson, how you talk!' says Laura. 'You oughter be ashamed of yourself!'

"But when I get the dish filled up with apples there ain't a Baldwin in all the lot that can compare with the bright red of Laura's cheeks. An' Laura knows it, too, an' she sees the mouse again, an' screams, and then the candle goes out, and we are in a dreadful stew.

"But I, bein' almost a man, contrive to bear up under it, and knowin' she is an orph'n, I comfort an' encourage

Laura the best I know how, and we are almost upstairs when Mother comes to the door and wants to know what has kep' us so long. Jest as if Mother doesn't know! Of course she does; an' when Mother kisses Laura good-by that night there is in the act a tenderness that speaks more sweetly than even Mother's words.

"It is so like Mother," mused Ezra; "so like her with her gentleness an' clingin' love. Hers is the sweetest picture of all, and hers the best love."

Dream on, Ezra; dream of the old home with its dear ones, its holy influences, and its precious inspiration!— Mother.

Dream on in the faraway firelight; and as the angel hand of memory unfolds these sacred visions, with thee and them shall abide, like a Divine Comforter, the spirit of Thanksgiving.

A Thanksgiving Fable

Oliver Herford

It was a hungry pussy cat upon Thanksgiving morn,
And she watched a thankful little mouse, that ate an
   ear of corn.
"If I ate that thankful little mouse, how thankful he
   should be,
When he has made a meal himself, to make a meal for
   me!
Then with his thanks for having fed, and his thanks
   for feeding me,
With all *his* thankfulness inside, how thankful I shall
   be!"
Thus mused the hungry pussy cat upon Thanksgiving
   Day;
But the little mouse had overheard and declined (with
   thanks) to stay.

The Huckabuck Family

Carl Sandburg

Jonas Jonas Huckabuck was a farmer in Nebraska with a wife, Mama Mama Huckabuck, and a daughter, Pony Pony Huckabuck.

"Your father gave you two names the same in front," people had said to him.

And he answered, "Yes, two names are easier to remember. If you call me by my first name Jonas and I don't hear you, then when you call me by my second name Jonas maybe I will.

"And," he went on, "I call my pony-face girl Pony Pony because if she doesn't hear me the first time she always does the second."

And so they lived on a farm where they raised popcorn, these three, Jonas Jonas Huckabuck, his wife, Mama Mama Huckabuck, and their pony-face daughter, Pony Pony Huckabuck.

After they harvested the crop one year they had the barns, the cribs, the sheds, the shacks, and all the cracks and corners of the farm all filled with popcorn.

"We came out to Nebraska to raise popcorn," said Jonas Jonas, "and I guess we got nearly enough popcorn this year for the popcorn poppers and all the friends and relations of all the popcorn poppers in these United States."

And this was the year Pony Pony was going to bake her first squash pie all by herself. In one corner of the corncrib, all covered over with popcorn, she had a secret, a big round squash, a fat yellow squash, a rich squash all spotted with spots of gold.

She carried the squash into the kitchen, took a long, sharp, shining knife, and then she cut the squash in the middle till she had two big half squashes. And inside, just like outside, it was rich yellow spotted with spots of gold.

And there was a shine of silver. And Pony Pony wondered why silver should be in a squash. She picked and plunged with her fingers till she pulled it out.

"It's a buckle," she said, "a silver buckle, a Chinese silver slipper buckle."

She ran with it to her father and said, "Look what I found when I cut open the golden-yellow squash spotted with gold spots—it is a Chinese silver slipper buckle."

"It means our luck is going to change, and we don't know whether it will be good luck or bad luck," said Jonas Jonas to his daughter Pony Pony Huckabuck.

Then she ran with it to her mother and said, "Look what I found when I cut open the yellow squash spotted with spots of gold—it is a Chinese silver slipper buckle."

"It means our luck is going to change, and we don't know whether it will be good luck or bad luck," said Mama Mama Huckabuck.

And that night a fire started in the barns, cribs, sheds, shacks, cracks, and corners, where the popcorn harvest was kept. All night long the popcorn popped. In the morning the ground all around the farmhouse and the barn was covered with white popcorn so it looked like a heavy fall of snow.

All the next day the fire kept on, and the popcorn popped till it was up to the shoulders of Pony Pony when she tried to walk from the house to the barn. And that night in all the barns, cribs, sheds, shacks, cracks, and corners of the farm the popcorn went on popping.

In the morning, when Jonas Jonas Huckabuck looked out of the upstairs window, he saw the popcorn popping and coming higher and higher. It was nearly up to the window.

Before evening and dark of that day Jonas Jonas Huckabuck, and his wife Mama Mama Huckabuck, and their daughter Pony Pony Huckabuck, all went away from the farm saying, "We came to Nebraska to raise popcorn, but this is too much. We will not come back till the wind blows away the popcorn. We will not come back till we get a sign and a signal."

They went to Oskaloosa, Iowa. And the next year

Pony Pony Huckabuck was very proud because when she stood on the sidewalks in the street she could see her father sitting high on the seat of a coal wagon, driving two big spanking horses hitched with shining brass harness in front of the coal wagon. And although Pony Pony and Jonas Jonas were proud, very proud all that year, there never came a sign, a signal.

The next year again was a proud year, exactly as proud a year as they spent in Oskaloosa. They went to Paducah, Kentucky; to Defiance, Ohio; Peoria, Illinois; Indianapolis, Indiana; Walla Walla, Washington.

And in all these places Pony Pony Huckabuck saw her father, Jonas Jonas Huckabuck, standing in rubber boots deep down in a ditch with a shining steel shovel shoveling yellow clay and black mud from down in the ditch high and high up over his shoulders. And although it was a proud year they got no sign, no signal.

The next year came. It was the proudest of all. This was the year Jonas Jonas Huckabuck and his family lived in Elgin, Illinois, and Jonas Jonas was watchman in a watch factory watching the watches.

"I know where you have been," Mama Mama Huckabuck would say of an evening to Pony Pony Huckabuck. "You have been down to the watch factory watching your father watch the watches."

"Yes," said Pony Pony. "Yes, and this evening when I was watching Father watch the watches in the watch factory I looked over my left shoulder and I saw a policeman with a star and brass buttons and he was watching me to see if I was watching Father watch the watches in the watch factory."

It was a proud year. Pony Pony saved her money. Thanksgiving came. Pony Pony said, "I am going to get a squash to make a squash pie." She hunted from one grocery to another; she kept her eyes on the farm wagons coming into Elgin with squashes.

She found what she wanted, the yellow squash spotted with gold spots. She took it home, cut it open, and saw the inside was like the outside, all rich yellow spotted with gold spots.

There was a shine like silver. She picked and plunged with her fingers and pulled and pulled till at last she pulled out the shine of silver.

"It's a sign; it is a signal," she said. "It is a buckle, a slipper buckle, a Chinese silver slipper buckle. It is the mate to the other buckle. Our luck is going to change. Yoo hoo! Yoo hoo!"

She told her father and mother about the buckle. They went back to the farm in Nebraska. The wind by this time had been blowing and blowing for three years, and all the popcorn was blown away.

"Now we are going to be farmers again," said Jonas Jonas Huckabuck to Mama Mama Huckabuck and to Pony Pony Huckabuck. "And we are going to raise cabbages, beets, and turnips; we are going to raise squash, rutabaga, pumpkins, and peppers for pickling. We are going to raise wheat, oats, barley, rye. We are going to raise corn such as Indian corn and kaffir corn—but we are *not* going to raise any popcorn for the popcorn pop-pers to be popping."

And the pony-face daughter, Pony Pony Huckabuck, was proud because she had on new black slippers, and around her ankles, holding the slippers on the left foot and the right foot, she had two buckles, silver buckles, Chinese silver slipper buckles. They were mates.

Sometimes on Thanksgiving Day and Christmas and New Year's she tells her friends to be careful when they open a squash.

"Squashes make your luck change good to bad and bad to good," says Pony Pony.

The Last Thursday in November

Grace Humphrey

Thanksgiving!

How much the very word says! Thanksgiving—you can feel the frosty air and the cold wind. You can see the bare trees against the gray sky. You can see the logs blazing on the hearth. You can hear the talk of travelers returning home for the day, the gay chatter and laughter of the young folks going to Grandfather's for this holiday.

Thanksgiving—guests coming up the walk with cheery greetings. There are the smiling faces of cousins, aunts, and uncles, full of gratitude and love. Thanksgiving— the one word tells it all.

Thanksgiving Day! Church in the morning, where members of all the different congregations meet for a union service. It is the one day of the year when they do this. Fitting it is that they give thanks, most fitting that they give thanks together.

After church comes the great event of the day, the Thanksgiving dinner. Vary as its details may in different years, in different sections of our country, it has always these fundamentals—turkey, cranberry sauce, and, to crown the feast, the golden pumpkin pie.

Sniff, sniff! Didn't you smell them early this morning during the half-hour of baking; smell the spices and the pumpkin and that special odor of flaky piecrust? Didn't you get the savor of the turkey when with flushed face Grandmother herself opened the oven door to baste it with the rich brown juice?

Turkey and cranberry sauce and pumpkin pie! A full table, not because we want so much to eat, but to symbolize the treasures of the generous earth! But turkey, cranberry sauce, pumpkin pie—it's a feast for the gods! A feast for Thanksgiving Day!

Although this November holiday is peculiarly American, the custom of celebrating the end of the harvest is not new. In England it was a famous holiday as far back as Alfred the Great's time.

And before there was an England the Romans had a harvest festival in honor of Ceres, a festival as old as the reign of Romulus. And before them the Greek women of Athens went each November in a gaily-bedecked procession to the temple of Demeter to give their thanks for the bountiful harvest with which she had blessed the land.

And before Greece the Jewish people had a similar festival at Jerusalem, called the Feast of Tabernacles. You can read of it in Plutarch, in Nehemiah and Judges,

and in the still older book of Exodus where Moses gives
directions for its observance.

But these celebrations of the end of harvest lacked
something of our American Thanksgiving. A full three
centuries old is this holiday. It was in December of 1621
that Governor Bradford announced that first day of rejoicing and thanksgiving in the little colony of Plymouth.

Not quite a year had passed since the *Mayflower*
anchored in the harbor of that rocky coast. What a year
it had been—a year of hardships in a new land, a year of
hunger and cold, of fear and constant sickness! The
supply of food grew less and less.

At one time all but seven persons in the colony were
ill. For the sick there was not the right kind of food.
Week by week Pilgrims had died till six and forty graves
were dug on the bluff overlooking the bay; dug there
and left level with the ground around, without any
mound of earth, without marking stones, lest the savage
red man learn how few the colonists were in numbers.

But with the spring even the disheartened among the
Pilgrims took heart once more. Go back to England,
three thousand miles away? Never! Here they could
worship God in their own way. Here they were free men.

With stout hearts, with steadfast faith the fifty colonists began to sow their seed. Twenty acres of corn they
put in, six of barley, and six of peas. Without ceasing
they cared for these fields. They watched the growth of
their crops anxiously. Well they knew that their lives
depended on a full harvest.

Spring and summer days flew by. The land was blessed

with showers and sunshine. Autumn came and dressed the woods in gorgeous colors—gold and crimson and brown. Their crops stood ready for the gathering. They reaped the fruit of their labors and housed it carefully for the winter.

In December Governor Bradford looked abroad on the little colony. Seven houses he counted, and four for community use. He gazed over the empty fields—the twenty acres whose golden shocks of corn had stood so close together, yielding a harvest such as old England never knew; the barley, too, had been a successful crop; but the peas had been planted too late and although they came up and bloomed, the hot summer sun withered the vines and parched them in the blossom.

"Yes," said the governor to himself, "after the 'starving time' we've lived through there's ample food on hand now for all of us. There's a peck of meal a week for each person, and since the harvest there's the same amount of Indian corn. We can face the winter and the future with lighter hearts. There'll be no second 'starving time'!"

If a man counted only hardships, Bradford's thought went on, this first year in Plymouth had a goodly number. If he counted only blessings, there were many, many. How could he best bring this truth home to his people?

"We have fasted together," he said in suggesting his plan. "Now let us feast together. Let us have a special day to give thanks for all the goodness of God. He has remembered us. We will remember Him."

The date was set for the thirteenth of the month.

"Let us invite our friends, the chief Massasoit and some of his braves," suggested Elder Brewster.

A runner went to Mount Hope to take the invitation to the Indians. Four men were sent fowling and such good fortune attended their shooting that in one day they got wild turkeys, partridges, and wood pigeons—enough to last the whole colony almost a week.

As soon as the plan for the feast day was announced the women set to work. Indeed it was a big task for the five of them, with a few young girls to help. There were pumpkin pies to be made and baked; turkeys to be plucked and dressed and stuffed with beechnuts; fish from the bay to be cleaned and broiled; barley bread and corn bread to be made; and many another good thing to be prepared. Busy, busy were the women and girls of Plymouth for days beforehand.

Early in the morning of the thirteenth, shortly after Captain Standish had fired off the sunrise gun, there came a great shout from the woods. Another shout, a shriek, and a wild whoop! Through the trees came a long line of Indians—the chief Massasoit and ninety of his braves.

In their best dress they came, with flourish of toma-hawks in honor of this feast day of their friends, the palefaces. Some of them had wide bands of black paint on their faces. Some had feathers stuck in their long,

straight black hair. Some wore the furry coat of a wildcat hanging from their shoulders. Some wore deerskins.

With the governor Captain Standish went to meet
them. Were they surprised at the number? Were they
dismayed at thought of the food necessary for ninety
visitors? Courteously they received their Indian guests.

Presently the beat of a drum announced morning
prayers. Every day began with this brief service. How
much more important on this feast day! The red men
looked on quietly, listening reverently while the stern,
grave Pilgrims prayed to the Great Spirit.

Then came breakfast—clam chowder with biscuit,
hasty pudding served with butter and treacle, for milk
they had none in Plymouth. At the north end of the
little village colonists and visitors assembled.

"Military exercises under the direction of Captain
Miles Standish," announced the governor.

The trumpets sounded. From the fort came the roll
of drums. Down the hill in soldierly array marched the
regiment of Plymouth—a regiment of twenty men. Over
them floated the flag of England.

March and countermarch, wheel and turn, rightabout-
face—through all the maneuvers Standish put his men
that morning. Frequently they discharged their muskets.
Once in answer there came a great roar from the four
cannon of the fort.

The red men danced, acted out stories, and played
games with the children. The colonists sang their songs.
A target was set up and the soldiers fired at it. The Indians standing in closer shot at it with their bows and

arrows. There was a friendly contest to see which side would make the larger score.

Meanwhile Mistress Brewster and Mistress Winslow with the three other women of the colony were hard at work. Remember Allerton and Mary Chilton, Priscilla and Desire and the younger girls helped as they could. Back and forth to the kitchen they went countless times, bearing pewter plates and heaping platters of good things to eat. At last dinner was announced.

What a meal that was, served at the long tables under the leafless trees! There were clams and scallops; wild turkey with Priscilla Mullins' famous dressing of beech-nuts; dumplings made of barley flour; pigeon pasty; bowls of salad wreathed with autumn leaves; baskets of wild grapes and plums; and the crown of every Thanksgiving dinner, the golden pumpkin pie.

Did the Indians surmise that their presence made extra work for the women of Plymouth? Did they wish to bring something of their own for the feast? The brother of Massasoit offered to lead a hunting party into the woods to look for deer. His braves knew well their favorite haunts. It would not take long.

"Yes, go," said Governor Bradford.

The next morning back came the red men with five deer. One they roasted whole. The others were cut up into steaks and smaller pieces for venison pie.

For two days more the feasting went on. Between English colonists and fierce Indians there was hearty fellowship and good will. Peace had been established on a firm foundation. Without such a peace the Pilgrims would never have won a footing on that bleak coast. Without it Plymouth could never have lived through that first year.

It was these friendly savages who told the newcomers how to use shad to fertilize their fields, when to plant corn—"as soon as the oak leaves are as big as a mouse's ear"—and where to find wild fruits and berries. Much was owing to the red men. Thrice welcome to the colony's feast day!

This is the story of that first Thanksgiving in faraway 1621. Since then in Plymouth, in the Massachusetts colony, there have been many such festivals. Sometimes there were two a year, if some special event made the leaders appoint a day of thanks and rejoicing. When hard times came and the outlook was disheartening they skipped a year. But from one generation to another in New England Thanksgiving has gone on and on.

The rest of the country was slow to adopt this beautiful custom. Here and there a governor proclaimed a day of thanksgiving for his state. But it was not permanent. There was no general celebration.

Soon after the middle of the nineteenth century a New England woman went from Boston to Philadelphia to become editor of the famous magazine called *Godey's Lady's Book*. She was greatly impressed by the fact that in Pennsylvania, and in other states as well, Thanksgiving Day was not observed. To her mind this was a state of affairs to be altered. At once she set to work.

She wrote to the governor of each state asking him to

appoint a day of thanksgiving and suggesting the last
Thursday in November. Some governors met her re-
quest. Some ignored it. The next year she wrote again,
and the next and the next. By 1859 Thanksgiving Day
was observed in all but two states.

Then came the Civil War. There was no time for a
celebration when everyone was occupied in work for the
soldiers. No one had heart for a festival when hearts
were saddened everywhere. But with the coming of peace
President Johnson proclaimed a day of thanksgiving for
the whole nation, in November of 1865. State after state
followed.

Since that year America has kept this holiday, proclaimed anew with each November by governors and
president.

The reasons for giving thanks in 1621 have remained
to this day, with many others added. It is a day when
the people recognize all the blessings of God and His
goodness to our land, a day to give thanks for bountiful
golden harvests, for peace and prosperity, for the general
welfare, a day for prayer and rejoicing.

Turkey and cranberry sauce and pumpkin pie!

What a tantalizing odor when the kitchen door is
opened for a moment!

There are voices from the gate and steps on the frosty
path. More guests are coming. For this is Thanksgiving
Day!

November

Elizabeth Coatsworth

November comes,
And November goes
With the last red berries
And the first white snows.

With night coming early
And dawn coming late,
And ice in the bucket
And frost by the gate.

The fires burn
And the kettles sing,
And earth sinks to rest
Until next spring.